PHYSICIAN BURNOUT

A GUIDE TO RECOGNITION AND RECOVERY

TOM MURPHY MD

Physician Burnout: A Guide to Recognition and Recovery
by Tom Murphy MD
© 2015 Heal Thyself MD LLC

Print ISBN: 978-1-61206-103-0
eBook ISBN: 978-1-61206-108-5

Lead Editor: Jennifer Regner
Interior design by: Fusion Creative Works, Fusioncw.com
Cover design by: Omni Designs and Fusion Creative Works
Project Management: Hannah Cross

For speaking or consulting on Physician Burnout or another partner with Heal
Thyself MD LLC, contact: Dr. Tom Murphy at tom@tommurphymd.com

Published by

AlohaPublishing.com

First Printing
Printed in the United States of America

To four very special physicians:

To my grandfather:
A man who epitomized what it means to be a doctor.

To my Uncle David:
A man who was unafraid to follow his dreams.

To my Uncle Tom:
A great physician who practiced medicine
in his own unique way.

To my father:
A man who courageously battled his own
demons of burnout. You are my hero.

And

To my wife Rachel:
You are my angel and my inspiration.
I never would have made it without you.

CONTENTS

SECTION 2: RECOGNIZING THE CAUSES

SECTION 3: SOLUTIONS TO BURNOUT

MOST MEN LEAD LIVES OF QUIET DESPERATION AND GO
TO THE GRAVE WITH THE SONG STILL IN THEM.

— HENRY DAVID THOREAU

INTRODUCTION

Time was baffling. It seemed like just yesterday, I sat in a posh auditorium in Chicago as an enthusiastic young adult during my first day of medical school orientation at Northwestern in 1995. Eighteen years later I was a forty-three-year-old burned out physician, practicing in Boise, Idaho, doing Google searches on the most effective way to end my life.

I survived my own journey through physician burnout and have now entered a new chapter in my life. I feel privileged to help physicians and hospital systems utilize new strategies and lifestyle plans to deal with the burnout epidemic. I speak, consult, and coach, sharing this story along the way. I am also going back into practice and it's joyful rather than what medicine had become for me.

As I learned about the problem of physician burnout, I have realized I am not alone. While researching this book, I realized burnout is not some psychological abnormality to be embarrassed to speak about in public—quite the contrary. Survey results in the past five years show 87% of American physicians experience symptoms of burnout.[1]

Burnout impacts not only the physician experiencing the problem, but also their families. And, it has dramatic implications for the patients the burned out physician treats. Increasing time constraints, burgeoning bureaucracy, increased patient expectations, and technological advances have made this challenging, stressful profession even more so. In fact, given the current state and the demands of the American healthcare system, I have realized burnout is an almost inevitable response.

Something needs to be done about it.

During my last several years of practice, each day seemed like a monumental struggle similar to that of the Greek mythological character Sisyphus. I tried simply to survive each overscheduled, jam-packed clinical day, but it was fruitless since I would just have to go through the same ordeal the next day and the day after that. Like Sisyphus, I felt condemned by the burden of rolling a heavy boulder up a monumental hill only to have it roll back down, repeating this process for the rest of eternity. Christina Maslach, one of the early pioneers in the field of job burnout, has succinctly characterized the problem as "an erosion of the human soul."[2]

It doesn't have to be that way. In this book, I have developed a series of initiatives at the individual, institutional, and medical educational levels to address the challenges of burnout. These initiatives will enhance productivity, improve physician wellbeing, and create better environments for patients.

Although many in the general public are not aware of the concept, most physicians are familiar with the term anhedonia—the loss of joy in previously pleasurable activities. As I did, a large number of physicians experienced this during the acute phases of burnout. We stopped enjoying activities such as running, yoga, reading, and spending time with our families. Our lives lost meaning.

Most people, physicians included, are unfamiliar with the term enantiadroma, meaning one emotion is replaced with its polar opposite—such as passion with hatred. At some point in almost every physician's career, we had a powerful desire to help others. When suffering burnout, many of us become so disillusioned by our failure to achieve these aspirations that our passion is replaced by a strong contempt, bordering on hatred, for the profession we chose and once loved.

My goal is to reignite that flame. I found a way to do it for myself with the help of several special people, and I want to share my experiences and new knowledge with you. Even severe burnout symptoms can be resolved, and you can recover.

By initiating changes within the medical community and culture, we can protect our newest physicians from the dangers of this condition. I can work with healthcare institutions to combat its development through policy and workplace modifications.

My sensible prescriptive plan addresses the growing problem of physician burnout from both individual and institutional standpoints. I want to give physicians a chance to rediscover a sense of joy, pleasure, and fulfillment from this noble profession.

SECTION 1

FOCUS ON THE PHYSICIAN

CHAPTER 1

PHYSICIAN BURNOUT IS AN EPIDEMIC

Physician burnout is characterized by severe physical and emotional distress, caused by the stresses and myriad of exacerbating factors that encompass medical practice in the modern American healthcare system. Merriam-Webster's dictionary defines burnout as, "the condition in which someone becomes very physically and emotionally tired after doing a difficult job for a long time." People in high-stress jobs such as law enforcement, military personnel, and physicians are particularly susceptible to developing this condition.

What are the signs of burnout?

If a physician shows an obvious change in demeanor or character, or overreacts to seemingly minor provocations with an outburst of temper or crying, this can be a sign of burnout. Changes in sleep habits, appetite or unintentional weight changes can also be clues.

My staff told me they knew I was burned out because relatively insignificant things caused me to become extremely agitated and emotional.

Burned out physicians also frequently lose interest in their favorite activities. Alcohol or illicit drug abuse are another indicator that a physician could possibly be attempting to self-medicate symptoms.

When my own burnout became extreme I did not enjoy the things I used to love, like running or spending time with my family.

Burnout is insidious; a creeping tide that slowly and steadily overwhelms a physician's life. It often starts as early as medical school—where a culture of self-reliance and independence is fostered. We learn we're not supposed to show signs of weakness or admit suffering; this is not our self-image as physicians.

Are you beginning to manage your heavy patient load by referring patients out to other specialists and ordering more diagnostic tests, hoping for quick easy answers rather than performing a thorough physical exam and history? The pressures on us are intense—many of us are just trying to keep our heads above water with new bureaucratic or administrative challenges added regularly.

Tragically, many of us choose to ignore the problem of burnout in ourselves, in stark contrast to how we would treat a sick patient. An ER physician would never tell a fifty-year-old male who presented with occasional stabbing sub-sternal chest pain to ignore it. An EKG, cardiac enzymes screen, and notification to the cardiologist on call would all follow—steps needed to address the emergency. Yet, we often convince ourselves our early warning signs of burnout will go away, or that we can just tough it out.

For such reasons, I refused to accept my own symptoms of burnout. They just became more extreme, to the point that I felt overwhelmed while driving in to work in the morning. I felt physically and emotionally fatigued even before the day began.

Worse, I had lost empathy for my patients. Once during an office visit a patient began to cry. Instead of considering what the patient might be feeling, I wondered how long this was going to take and how it would impact my schedule. Was I going to fall behind? I made the appropriate gestures, a hand on the shoulder, an attempt to find a tissue, but I was just going through the motions. I had nothing to give them, emotionally.

Sometimes others can recognize when we are experiencing burnout. A spouse or colleague may identify these signs which we do not—or perhaps choose not—to see. One day, when I felt completely overwhelmed by burnout, I went into an exam room to see the friendly face of a psychiatrist who was one of my patients.

As I began to ask him how he was doing and started to go through the details of his case, he politely interrupted me and said, "Wait. I want you to sit down and take some deep breaths. You look terrible. I have been exactly where you have been myself. Let's take a minute or two and get you in a better place before we talk about me." We chatted for several minutes. His recognition of my situation and sharing with me some of his own experiences were invaluable. This was a kind and helpful gesture, and it was the first wake up call to me that I was grappling with the issue of burnout.

Do you find yourself asking what happened to the passion and enthusiasm you had as a medical student? Do you mock your patients, or find you have lost all empathy for them? Do you find you no longer engage with your family, lack focus, energy, passion, and are going through the motions robotically?

If some of this sounds uncomfortably familiar, you are not alone. If you are a physician experiencing burnout, statistically you are among the majority of your American colleagues.

CHAPTER 2

BURNOUT IS DIFFERENT THAN STRESS

Stress is a transient reaction to a difficult situation. Most people can have a very stressful day at work, come home, exercise, spend time with family, and feel better. What distinguishes stress from burnout is that you can't recover from burnout, or recharge for the next day, in a short period of time. Burned out physicians are not able to recharge prior to the next workday and often drive into work feeling overwhelmed and exhausted, dreading the day that lies ahead.

The normal, everyday decisions a physician makes to diagnose and improve their patients' health are stressful, in part, because the cost of being wrong is so high. Also, taking care of and diagnosing sick and emotionally vulnerable people requires a great deal of energy. It is almost impossible for a physician not to experience some stress each and every day.

Further compounding the problem are the added work-related demands imposed on physicians outside their daily work schedule. Being on call, keeping up to date with new medical advances, and studying to maintain board certification all prevent physicians from escaping work when at home.

Many times during my residency and training, I was subjected to stress and felt worn down, but I was always resilient enough to recover after a good night's sleep, a vacation, or time away from the hospital.

During my working career I crossed over into different territory, where time away from work was only a reprieve. I came home psychologically drained every day. I had no emotional resilience for response to the normal hassles of everyday life outside of work. And, I didn't feel my batteries were sufficiently recharged when I went back to work.

An analogy between burnout and stress can be made with sleep. If a person misses a night of sleep, they usually can make up for it or recover the next night. If a person misses three or four days of sleep or becomes chronically sleep deprived, their body will eventually break down and they will suffer significant physiologic distress. If a physician experiences repeated, unending stresses at work with no relief, as can happen in modern medicine, they lose the ability to recover, and cross over into the territory of burnout.

CHAPTER 3

LET'S LOOK AT BURNOUT SYMPTOMS

Three defining symptoms characterize physician burnout. These are emotional exhaustion, depersonalization, and lack of meaning from work. If a physician is suffering all or even just one of these symptoms, he or she likely is experiencing underlying burnout. The three symptoms can be measured by an industry standard survey known as the Maslach Burnout inventory.[3]

EMOTIONAL EXHAUSTION

Physicians suffering from emotional exhaustion have invested so much energy into taking care of their patients and worrying about their patients' problems that they have nothing left for themselves or their families. Emotional exhaustion is akin to a car that has run out of gas.

When I was really burned out, I reacted to my daughter coming down with the flu as if it was a calamity. If I had a flat tire, it was the end of the world. Any work-related event became a mountain—a frivolous patient complaint was disastrous, a lost dictation I had to repeat was a tragedy of monumental proportions. Each little event became more evidence of the hopeless situation I felt trapped in.

Dr. Don Jacobson, a psychiatrist and burnout specialist, described this hopeless entrapment response as learned helplessness. Learned helplessness, which can be a symptom of depression, can occur when a subject experiences a repeated averse stimulus. A subject responding this way will eventually stop trying to avoid the negative stimulus and behave as if unable to change the situation, even if there are opportunities to do so.

An analogy to the emotional exhaustion experienced by burned-out physicians comes from "The Crucible" by Arthur Miller. In the book, the innocent Giles Cory refused to plead as a witch. Mr. Cory was sentenced to *peine forte et dure*, a punishment carried out by placing successive rocks on a board laid across the prisoner's body, until he pled or was pressed to death. Just as with Giles Cory, exhausted and burned out physicians are asked to accept "more weight", and they may continue to accept it with perilous results.

DEPERSONALIZATION

The second telltale sign of burnout is depersonalization. With depersonalization, one becomes detached from others. Physicians experiencing this symptom view their patients as objects or things rather than actual human beings. Physicians experiencing depersonalization have stated they felt robotic. Their interactions with patients focus primarily on controlling how much time they will be forced to spend with the patient, instead of addressing the patient's underlying problem or medical condition. It's as if the names on the physician's daily schedule are no longer people, but rather tasks to be checked off a list. Physicians have described the experience of depersonalization as if they were participating in a movie or TV show; they are acting out a role that doesn't seem authentic to them. The physician is cognitively present but emotionally absent.

Depersonalization is a coping mechanism, albeit a dysfunctional one, in which physicians try to protect themselves from their patients by distancing themselves and emotionally detaching themselves from them.

Depersonalization is very common in modern medicine. Doctors suffering from burnout can become extremely cynical and jaded in part as a defense mechanism. They don't like it when patients are noncompliant or rude or needy. They seek emotional protection from them by detaching from them. One could argue that the very process of medical training serves as a fertile training ground for depersonalization. If doctors invest too much psychological energy in patients, then they would be completely overwhelmed every time one of them became severely ill or died.

Depersonalization takes this notion to an extreme in that a physician loses empathy and is unable to feel compassionately toward his patients, nor towards himself. Compassion and caring are replaced by caustic jokes and sardonic remarks in the break room. One example that exemplifies depersonalization occurred when I saw a physician dismiss a patient who had actually called to thank the physician for his care. After getting off the phone the doctor shook his head and said, "Senile old joker."

Depersonalization can also be described as "compassion fatigue." A perfect example of compassion fatigue occurred when a burned out physician told me of an encounter he recently had with a patient. The physician stopped by the patient's room and informed him that an MRI had confirmed that the patient had a mild stroke. When the patient tried to elicit more information, the physician grew frustrated because he was behind schedule and felt he had already provided the pertinent information. The patient then began to cry and the physician became exasperated, frustrated because the matter was taking up a lot of his time. The physician told me he was incapable of putting himself in the patient's position and that his "empathy reserves" were depleted. After this episode, the physician came and talked to me, eventually seeking help.

LACK OF PERSONAL ACCOMPLISHMENT

The final characteristic of burnout is the loss of any sense of personal accomplishment or satisfaction from work. Many physicians have described a youthful idealism from their time as medical students which has been lost or shrouded by the stress and anxiety of the modern medical practice. The job has become solely a source of income accompanied by the threat of litigation from any missteps. A physician is no longer proactively looking for solutions, and is just trying not to miss anything, checking off the necessary boxes on a computer monitor. He is in survival mode.

Physicians in this stage may begin to doubt the quality of the care they are providing, in addition to their growing belief that their work lacks meaning. Many physicians report that they went into medicine to help others, but the joy of that ethos was lost during the course of their career.

On a personal level, when I lost my joy in practicing medicine, going to work literally felt like a prison sentence. While helping other physicians navigate through burnout, I have been amazed at how many times I hear the exact same analogy. One physician told me, "Driving to the office every day was a jail sentence, but I told myself at least I have my weekends and nights off. I hope to retire in my mid-fifties, so I have about a fourteen year sentence left."

SYMPTOM SUMMARY

Physician burnout has traditionally been characterized by one or more of these three symptoms: emotional exhaustion, depersonalization, and a lack of personal accomplishment or joy from work. A physician with burnout may experience all three of these symptoms simultaneously or only one at any particular time. Various scales have been used to measure burnout, but identification of a physician with one of these symptoms is enough to categorize a physician as burned out.

Another important point is burnout does not equal depression. Although many physicians who are burned out may have coexisting depression, burnout is caused by external environmental stressors as opposed to depression, which is a medical illness intrinsic to that individual. Burnout is related to work environment. Depressed individuals can be lethargic and plagued by guilt, whereas job burnout is more likely to be characterized by disappointment and dissatisfaction. Although depression and burnout obviously have overlapping symptoms, the two syndromes are not synonymous.

CHAPTER 4

STATISTICS AND STORIES
THAT HIT HOME

Physician burnout is a rapidly growing epidemic in our healthcare system. Numerous articles about the topic have appeared in USA Today, The New York Times, and the Wall Street Journal. A nationally recognized expert in the field of physician burnout, John-Henry Pfifferling, has estimated that 80% of physicians will experience burnout at some point in their professional careers.[4]

Physicians with the highest rates of burnout are in family practice, ER, and internal medicine. These physicians on the frontlines of care are forced to deal with the lion's share of paperwork, regulatory burdens, and roadblocks from private insurers, compared to their counterparts in subspecialties. Yet, despite these added burdens, physicians in primary care are less well paid and work longer hours than their subspecialty colleagues.

Studies have demonstrated between 46%[5] and 87%[6] of American physicians have experienced signs of burnout recently.

GENDER DIFFERENCES

Female doctors are slightly more likely to report burnout than their male counterparts.[7] Female physicians who experience burnout are more likely to report symptoms of exhaustion as a consequence of burnout in contrast to their male counterparts who are more likely to experience symptoms of depersonalization.[8]

AGE DIFFERENCES

Burnout peaks in midlife but can occur at any time, including during medical school. In fact, one recent study showed that 50% of medical students experience some symptom of burnout and 11% had active suicidal thoughts.[9] Burned out physicians are also less likely to engage in healthy restorative activities including vacations, exercise, and volunteering, which may serve to exacerbate the underlying problem.

PROFESSION DIFFERENCES

Other professions create conditions for development of burnout. Fields that show the highest burnout rates are public service providers, such as teachers, police, and healthcare workers. Statistically, physicians experience a much higher rate of burnout compared to other working adults in the US population. Doctors also report a greater work and life imbalance compared to other working adults in the US, and studies have shown physicians work significantly more hours than their peers in other professions. In contrast to other professions, such as the law or business, where an advanced postgraduate degree reduces burnout rates compared to the general population, a medical degree is the only postgraduate degree that actually increases the risk for burnout.[5]

Over 75% of physicians are pessimistic about the future of medicine, and over 80% agree the medical profession is in decline.[10] A majority of physicians would not recommend the career to their children, and over a third of physicians would not choose medicine as a career if they were given the option of doing it over again. A 2012 study by the Urban Institute showed over half of middle-aged physicians and 30% of physicians between ages thirty-five to forty-nine who provided frontline care, such as general practitioners and internists, plan to quit the profession within the next five years. Finally, over 60% of physicians would retire today if they had the economic means to do so.[11]

Based on a statistical analysis of burnout studies as well as my personal experiences with numerous physicians, it's apparent that a majority of physicians practicing medicine in the US walk into work every day feeling burned out. From a patient standpoint, the next physician who walks through the door to see you is more likely than not to be experiencing some degree of burnout.

If a similar proportion of the general public were suffering from the symptoms of burnout, the story would be everywhere and labeled as an epidemic; however, medicine is a culture where physicians are taught from the very first stages of their training to project an image of strength and to be tough. In fact, the phrase the "lone ranger" is often used to describe physicians attempting to be strong, and refusing to acknowledge the problem of underlying burnout. A physician in his fifties who I am currently working with summarized this sentiment well: "I can remember the phrase used at Vanderbilt when we were on call thirty-six hours and off for twelve hours, sometimes for months. Whenever we would pass each other in the hall, we would say "Got to love it," to each other.

CHAPTER 5

HOW SERIOUS IS PHYSICIAN BURNOUT?

BURNOUT AFFECTS EVERYONE

Burnout has major ramifications not just for physicians and their family members, but for the patients relying on them and the institutions hiring them as well. Burned out physicians are more likely to commit medical errors and to be sued for malpractice. A New York Times editorial recently described an example in which a physician suffering from burnout dismissively misdiagnosed a patient with a pinched nerve when the patient in fact had an underlying tumor causing his problem.[12]

From an institutional standpoint, several major problems arise from physician burnout, including increased physician turnover and decreased production from burned out doctors. Also, physicians with burnout have a higher rate of absenteeism. Patient satisfaction scores tend to be lower for burned out doctors than those of their peers. This all makes sense. An exhausted physician experiencing feelings of depersonalization is much more likely to commit an error, become short with coworkers, and provide suboptimal care for his or her patients in comparison to a physician who enjoys coming to work every day. Psychiatrist Don Jacobson describes the situation adroitly, "Happy doctors make for happy patients and vice versa."

Burned out physicians affect staff morale and turnover, which negatively influences all aspects of the health care system—from the hiring institution to the patients. This was exemplified in a recent conversation I had with a nurse in a large healthcare system, working for a doctor suffering telltale signs of burnout. He is prone to emotional outbursts, has low production numbers, and often mocks his patients behind their backs. As a result, his staff turnover rate is high and his patient satisfaction scores are low. The nurse I spoke with plans to leave as soon as she finds another opportunity. Each time a nurse quits, a replacement must be hired and trained at considerable expense. This in turn reduces the physician's patient volume, eroding his production numbers further, and creating a negative self-sustaining feedback loop.

PHYSICIAN BURNOUT IS AN EPIDEMIC

Burnout is a very common problem—an actual epidemic! A majority of the physicians I know, who are friends or colleagues, are burned out. I recently met with a very good friend, with whom I did my medical residency, at an alternative career conference for physicians. He told me he just does not enjoy practicing medicine anymore in today's environment.

Many American physicians do not like the transformational shifts that have occurred in our healthcare system over the last ten years. During this time we as physicians have experienced a severe loss of control, developed a feeling of powerlessness, and things just seem to get worse every day. My physician colleagues have encouraged me to continue to educate others about burnout and to spread the word about how common the problem is so other physicians will realize that they are **not** alone.

CHAPTER 6

COMMON BEHAVIORAL SIGNS OF BURNOUT

PERFECTIONISM

Burned out physicians tend to be burdened by a sense of perfectionism. They also begin to self-identify with their job—they don't think of being a physician as a profession, but as an identity—it is who they are. Many of these physicians, as a result, weigh themselves down with impossible "should" lists. They usually don't prioritize the list, realizing they probably can't complete everything. When they don't successfully accomplish everything, they feel guilty. If they do accomplish everything on their list, they get home at nine pm at night, completely exhausted, and with another to-do list of "shoulds" staring them in the face for tomorrow.

OBSESSION WITH NEGATIVE EVENTS

Burned out physicians have a propensity to pick out the negative detail in any situation and then obsess about it. In my own experience, I could have a negative patient interaction in my morning clinic that would become the entire focus of my day. I might have twenty great visits after that, but I would relive the one negative experience for days. Similarly, I knew a badly burned out surgeon who became so fixated on one patient's minor post-operative complication that it affected his ability to practice.

JUDGING AND SELF-LABELING

Physicians will self-label in an unfair and overly harsh manner. I might think to myself, "I'm a bad doctor because my treatments aren't helping this rheumatoid arthritis patient." Mental health experts have told me it's a sign that a physician is deep into the burnout process and needs assistance when they begin to mentally label their patients. For example, when I was really burned out, I used to mentally judge my patients with derogatory labels. I had lost all sense of empathy. When physicians judge and label their patients in this manner, they likely are not providing optimal care and are displaying signs of depersonalization and detachment toward their patients.

MISPLACED RESPONSIBILITY

Finally, many burned out physicians assume personal responsibility for events that are beyond their control. For example, sometimes a patient would experience a known possible side effect from a medication I had prescribed, and I would fault myself for this inconvenience. This type of behavior is like a pilot who, scheduled to fly a plane that is delayed due to bad weather, blames himself or herself for the inconvenience. If you often feel this way, ask colleagues or friends close to you for their perspective—this may provide a signal that you need to ask for help to regain a more balanced view.

CHAPTER 6

I have seen primary care doctors who blame themselves on some level because a patient continues to engage in unhealthy habits such as smoking or alcoholism, despite repeated attempts at intervention. Unfortunately, part of modern medicine is accepting less than perfect outcomes for some patients.

As perfectionist physicians we have a dangerous propensity to assume everything is our fault. I have encountered many instances of physicians expressing profound personal guilt and sorrow about a bad patient outcome that they have carried sometimes for over thirty years. I certainly had such feelings; learning to process these feelings can be a big part of the recovery phase.

If some of these descriptions sound familiar to you either as a physician, or as a friend or family member of a physician, I encourage you to take or pass on the burnout self-assessment questionnaire we have developed which can be found in the next chapter, and also on TomMurphyMD.com.

CHAPTER 7

LET'S SEE WHERE YOU ARE: 25 QUESTION ASSESSMENT

		Yes/No
1.	Do you feel completely drained and exhausted some days?	
2.	Have experienced sleep disturbance, such as insomnia, recently?	
3.	Do you dread your job and feel unhappy driving into work?	
4.	Do minor stressors, such as an ill child at home or a flat tire, seem magnified and overwhelming to the point they feel like the proverbial "last straw"?	
5.	Have you verbalized out loud to a friend or spouse a phrase similar to: "I hate my job" "I can't handle this anymore" "I hate working at this place"?	
6.	Have coworkers, friends or a spouse expressed concern about your wellbeing?	
7.	Do you feel trapped in your current job or situation?	
8.	Have you ever become so fed up that you considered leaving the practice of medicine?	

		Yes/No
9.	Have you ever considered suicide?	
10.	Are you depressed on Sunday nights at the prospect of going in to work the next day?	
11.	Do you ever feel disgust, contempt, or disregard for your patients?	
12.	Have you recently lost your temper, either at home or at work, over a minor provocation?	
13.	Do you wish you had never gone to medical school and dream about alternative scenarios of what you would have done with your life if you had not become a doctor? Do you feel you have chosen the wrong profession?	
14.	Do you feel you lack control over your schedule and your working environment?	
15.	Do you consider yourself a perfectionist at work, where everything has to be done just right?	
16.	Do you feel a sense of injustice and powerlessness in your relationship with your employer?	
17.	Do you ever use alcohol or another substance as a means of escape?	
18.	Do you feel you function in "survival mode" at work?	
19.	Do you feel really depressed at the end of a week of vacation, rather than recharged, as you consider the prospect of going back into work?	
20.	Do you feel you are not getting what you want out of your job?	
21.	Are you perpetually worried about potential litigation and the ever-present threat of a medical malpractice lawsuit during every interaction you have with a patient?	

		Yes/No
22.	Do you feel negatively about your job?	
23.	Do you feel less sympathetic toward patients than you once were?	
24.	Do you feel misunderstood or underappreciated by your employer?	
25.	After work, do you need more time than you did in the past in order to relax and feel normal?	

If you answered yes to many of these questions, it's very likely you are experiencing symptoms of burnout. And, it is time to acknowledge the problem and do something about it immediately.

CHAPTER 8

FACTORS CONTRIBUTING TO BURNOUT

Burnout is caused by a multitude of factors. Many of us came to medicine as a "calling," a Norman Rockwell view of the general practitioner. We learned along the way that taking care of sick, vulnerable patients and diagnosing their illnesses and issues is a very stressful undertaking. Doing this well is, in many respects, in direct conflict with the realities of modern American medicine.

Also, many good and caring physicians simply can't stop taking their work home with them, worrying about a complicated case, concerned they may have missed something in that sick child they saw earlier in the day. That responsibility is always there, on weekends, at night, on vacation.

The following common issues potentially contribute to a physician's work- and stress-load, and can lead to burnout. They can also be starting points for solutions and prevention. If any of these are sore spots for you, make a note of them. They will be discussed in more detail in the next section.

TIME CONSTRAINTS

Today, we work in a volume-based practice model which rewards us financially for seeing as many patients in as short a time as possible. In fact, "good" work is often penalized. Any time spent establishing personal rapport with a patient, asking about their kids, or explaining about a disease process over the phone further reduces the number of patients that can be seen and billed.

This volume-based model forces us to choose between being a good person and doctor, or being paid appropriately. Moreover, being a good doctor is based on building a personal relationship between the physician and patient. And that takes time.

Many physicians have become demoralized as the proverbial seven minute visit and other time restrictions has limited their ability to provide the quality care they would ideally like to for their patients. Pamela Wible, an expert on the topic of physician burnout, summarizes the change in medicine from the slower-paced 1960s and 1970s to the present succinctly: "We have gone from a relationship-driven profession to a production-driven profession."[13]

BUREAUCRACY

The bureaucratic workload in modern American medicine has become incomprehensible. Physicians have huge amounts of regulatory and paperwork requirements that they must fulfill. Every patient interaction requires onerous computer documentation. It seems physicians face new and daunting bureaucratic challenges almost every week.

Further compounding the problem, physicians are rapidly losing autonomy and control in all aspects of their practice.

Cookbook medicine has become commonplace. They are told which guidelines to follow, even when they can see clear and obvious contraindications.

Insurance companies can bury doctors in a labyrinth of prior authorization requirements. Physicians are not paid for this paperwork and it detracts from time they could otherwise spend with their patients and families. The irrational office visit coding rules the modern healthcare system dictates, such as "meaningful use," are an added frustration that can be the proverbial paperwork last straw. Trying to understand the requirements involved in medical billing and coding makes something like tax law look simple. Many physicians come in on their off days and weekends to do paperwork.

My dad, a retired radiologist, recently went to a dermatologist for a basal skin cancer removal. During the visit, he was asked if he felt "safe" at home and if he used condoms with sexual activity. By mandating that we ask about everything, we are less able to focus on the important things that necessitated the office visit in the first place.

LITIGATION

The ever-present and very real threat of litigation oppresses every physician. Unfortunately, the fear of litigation affects every aspect of patient care. Physicians often order tests their patients don't always need, admit patients to the hospital unnecessarily, or send them for additional consultations in order to protect themselves. Many obstetricians have switched exclusively to gynecology and stopped practicing obstetrics because of litigation fear.

PHYSICIAN BURNOUT

Every physician I know has either a personal story involving unnecessary litigation or knows a colleague who has gone through such an experience. Physicians can be sued out of greed, even when nothing was done wrong clinically. Lawsuits are often not remotely related to quality of care. The two best physicians I know have been sued three times collectively.

PERSONAL FINANCES

Many physicians are weighed down with medical school debt and don't have a long term financial plan. They are simply in survival mode, existing paycheck to paycheck.

My experience has been that physicians who are deeply burned out and also in financial debt often are unsure of exactly how much they owe. They are simply trying to pay off the credit card bills, student loans, the mortgage, and to just make it until the next paycheck. This uncertainty adds to their stress, and makes them feel trapped in their jobs.

PATIENT SATISFACTION SCORES

Physicians also are judged by patient satisfaction scores. These are frequently not a fair or appropriate way to critique the care they are delivering. Often, disgruntled patients give a doctor low satisfaction scores exactly because he has done the medically appropriate thing.

For example, I spent over an hour explaining to a patient why she did not need an antibiotic for a viral infection and how prescribing one could actually be bad for her health. She subsequently filed a patient complaint and gave me a very low satisfaction score. Another time I received an abysmal patient satisfaction score because the patient did not like the wallpaper in my office.

CALL SCHEDULES

Second only to the daily stress of an overloaded patient schedule, a physician's call schedule causes a critical loss of control, autonomy, and quality of life. The added responsibility can prevent real enjoyment and relaxation during a physician's time off.

People don't keep a nine-to-five schedule when they are sick or get injured. This fact is one aspect that makes practicing medicine stressful. Rendering clinical judgments over the phone for patients without having access to their history or lab results creates additional stress due to potential errors and litigation risk.

MEDICAL MISINFORMATION AND INTERNET ACCESS

Modern technology has created new challenges for physicians. Patients are much better informed, and sometimes misinformed, because they have access to the Internet. Patients become convinced they are the expert because they read something on WebMD (webMD.com) or saw a Dr. Oz show. They may become alarmed or convinced they have a disease and want additional testing based on something they read on the Internet. Too often, the information is superficial or sometimes just flat-out erroneous.

PROBLEM PATIENTS

Noncompliant, threatening, or narcotic-seeking patients are another added stress. Some patients continue to drink and smoke themselves to death despite their physicians repeated attempts at intervention. Physicians occasionally have to deal with patients who have physically threatened them. And there may be no more frustrating patient than the one who wants an apparently unjustified prescription for narcotics.

BOARD CERTIFICATION REQUIREMENTS

Maintaining board certification requires strenuous examinations and preparation including long hours of study. New requirements for maintenance of certification (MOC) as well as keeping up with new advances in one's medical field consume a physician's already limited time and energy.

PATIENT EMAILS

With increased access to email, many physicians now receive patient emails outside of office visits. In some cases, this mode of communication may save time by avoiding misunderstandings if a patient can get a simple question answered rapidly, or by making follow-up appointments unnecessary. If a staff nurse or medical assistant screens these emails, they can be an efficient extension of healthcare.

However, this new communication avenue can also be quite burdensome. One physician I work with has over two thousand patients and was recently told that she was obligated to respond personally to all email-related questions they had. To meet this new requirement, she was forced to spend time in the evening emailing patients rather than being with her family. The demands of our profession are changing so fast that doctors are having difficulty keeping up.

CHAPTER 9

IT'S NOT WORTH YOUR LIFE

No discussion of physician burnout would be complete without mentioning the alarming number of documented physician suicides. The medical profession has the highest rate of suicide among the various professions. According to the American Foundation for Suicide Prevention, male physicians have a 70% higher rate of suicide than their counterparts in the general population while female physicians have an astounding 250 to 400% higher rate of suicide than their counterparts in other professions.

Every year 300 to 400 American physicians choose to end their lives. These numbers are likely an underestimate. Suicide is often underreported by colleagues as a cause of death. Pamela Wible relates a tale of two male colleagues from her medical school class who subsequently took their own lives, but whose deaths were listed as accidental drug overdoses.[14] Does it seem plausible that a physician would accidently overdose? As Dr. Wible says, physicians prescribe and dose medications for a living.[15] Physicians also have ready access to potentially lethal toxic medications. Firearms and medication overdose are the most common form of physician suicide.[16]

PHYSICIAN BURNOUT

The tragic problem of physician suicide requires immediate action. As a society, we cannot ignore this disastrous trend among some of our best and brightest.

The medical profession is by default a demanding and stressful occupation, and medical students are taught to be "good soldiers" early on in medical school. Nationally recognized physician burnout psychologist Herdley Paulini has emphasized that the "lone ranger" culture so prevalent in the medical profession creates a barrier, and physicians are afraid or extremely reluctant to seek the help they so desperately need. At the time of their suicide, most physicians who attempt this desperate act are not under psychiatric care.

Physicians view asking for help as a sign of weakness or even failure, and that is difficult for a profession that attracts perfectionists. They want to be the perfect role models with ideal mental and physical health for their patients.

I have often seen colleagues who model the behavior they learned during residency and apply this to their working career. They work through lunch, stay late at night and go in on weekends. And we are even more negligent about our mental health. We "play through the pain," because that is what we are taught to do. This is in direct contrast to the advice we give our patients.

The medical profession must work to destigmatize depression and burnout issues, and to educate young doctors on how to avoid them. We must start valuing our own needs as much as we value the needs of our patients.

What can you do? The physician community needs to create an atmosphere of support for troubled colleagues. A self-evaluation assessment designed to identify issues of professional frustration, burnout, and depression should be included in "burnout prevention" classes and career management courses.

Why might you suspect someone is in danger? If that physician is increasingly isolating himself from friends and family, or showing inappropriate outbursts of temper, he may be in significant distress. Finally, you may see the symptoms of alcohol and drug abuse, often a sign of an underlying problem.

If you know or suspect someone is in trouble, reach out to them in whatever way you can.

Finally, as Dr. Wible and others have pointed out, we need to remove the fear that reporting an illness will result in a significantly negative impact on our careers.

Some state medical boards will initiate disciplinary action against a physician with an addictive illness or mental health diagnosis. Following questions about drug and alcohol abuse and felonies, virtually every state medical licensing board has a question similar to this: "Have you ever had a medical condition or been treated for a problem that could hinder or impair your ability to provide patient care?"

When state boards deal harshly with a physician who is seeking help, it sends a wave of fear through the community, and physicians in distress are loathe to report a problem, as they fear it will have implications on their licensure, livelihood, and ability to practice.

If you are contemplating suicide, know that you can escape the trap you feel has taken away your choices. Think of your family and treat this as an emergent medical issue. Recognize that you are experiencing a transient medical illness—and with appropriate intervention you can and will return to a happier, better state.

In upcoming chapters, we will address in detail the causes of physician burnout and look at the far-reaching consequences of this problem.

CHAPTER 10

CLOSING THE GAP BETWEEN EXPECTATION AND REALITY

"You don't need to see different things,
but rather to see things differently."

— **Lama Surya Das,** *Awakening the Buddha Within*

At the core of burnout lies the conflict between our expectations and reality. To move past your anger or frustration, you must first acknowledge the realities of the current climate. Then, either change your expectations and accept the situation as it is, or change your working environment. Many physicians are stuck in a quagmire, where they do neither. As a result they cannot move forward.

My goal is to show you how to change things at work, and how to proactively manage your professional career. Some of your expectations must also change if you want to be successful in the current medical climate. You don't have to abandon all of your expectations and ideals, but some realities in modern medicine are here to stay, and we cannot change them.

When students first enter medical school, they think they understand the obstacles they will need to overcome. Similarly, residents have a rough gauge of what they think real-world practice will be like.

However, when they are confronted by the realities of today's practice environment, such as litigation, increased patient expectations and patient loads, decreased compensation, and a lack of public respect for the medical profession—all while trying to navigate a work-life family balance—young physicians can feel overwhelmed. Medicine is often not the richly rewarding profession we envisioned it to be when we entered medical school.

Similarly, older physicians in their forties and fifties have witnessed the transition that has occurred since they first started to practice, and they grieve over the vestiges of a prior time.

Physicians often experience tremendous stress and sadness because of the huge mismatch between what they thought medicine would be and what it actually has become. The public's respect and trust in physicians has seriously eroded for a multitude of reasons. Inflation-adjusted compensation for physicians is decreasing compared to prior eras, such as the seventies.[17] Patients are not always the benevolent, thankful individuals they were envisioned to be; they can be rude, belligerent, and hostile.

In many ways, we are held to almost impossible standards. Occasionally, we conclude some hospital administrators seem more concerned about the bottom line than about patient care. We are buried in an avalanche of paperwork, pushed to spend as little time as possible per patient, and are frequently burdened by complex electronic medical record (EMR) systems. On the other hand, it seems no patient should ever die or have a difficult diagnosis. While being held to this higher level of accountability, physician autonomy and control over patient care has been reduced.

Just as an actual Big Mac at McDonalds does not match the mouthwatering picture of the one shown in the commercial, modern medicine is not what we thought it was going to be. In order to survive in this environment, you have to do everything you can to maximize your working efficiency and effectiveness, while preserving your peace of mind and health. We will discuss measures that can be taken in more detail in later chapters.

For example, EMR systems appear to be permanent despite the fact that these systems can be laborious, time-consuming and frustrating. Rather than wasting time and energy on anger and frustration at the burden caused by EMR, do everything possible to maximize your use of your EMR system. Also, look for time-saving benefits your system may have. As recently described in a RAND survey, the benefits of an EMR system include the improved tracking of guideline-based care markers and allowing easier access to other provider's notes (by eliminating the problem of illegible handwriting).[18]

If you are weighed down by a heavy patient load and you feel you don't have enough time to see each patient and do a good job by your standards, then you should take steps to decrease your patient volume.

It is raining on the modern American healthcare system. You can choose to either scream at the thunderclouds and get soaked or opt to take an umbrella, put on a rain jacket and boots, and navigate your way to the best of your ability.

CHAPTER 11

BARRIERS TO GETTING THROUGH BURNOUT

Every person carries with them almost subconscious philosophies and cultural filters that guide their behavior—their values and motivations, in other words. When these personal philosophies lead a person to make destructive choices, they can be difficult to pinpoint as the source of the problem—and they become barriers to improvement or healing instead of behavioral guides.

For large institutions, the business model, financial goals, leadership attitudes, legal and healthcare industry regulations are among the many factors that create workplace philosophies and cultural filters. These can also be barriers to adaptations the institution needs to make to deal with issues such as burnout.

Although doctors have a lower risk of mortality from cancer and heart disease compared to the general population, they have a significantly higher risk of dying from suicide, a desperate final solution to a treatable condition: depression.[19] In my personal experience, I have noticed that although doctors generally recognize the importance of their physical health and make lifestyle choices such as exercising and not smoking, they seem to be at high risk for depression and prone to substance abuse. Logically, you would expect doctors to recognize their own illnesses and seek treatment. However, a multitude of barriers prevent them from addressing issues of substance abuse, mental health, or burnout.

PERSONAL OR INTRINSIC BARRIERS TO TREATMENT

I often came home from work angry and unable to tune out the annoyances and stress of my work day. In my mind, medicine was always supposed to come first. Sir William Osler, a patron saint and guiding father of modern day internal medicine once said, "What about the wife and babies if you have them? Leave them! Heavy are the responsibilities to yourself, to the profession and to the public. Your wife will be glad to bear her share of the sacrifices you make." This is where the culture of medicine must change. Families and a physician's health must come first.

We physicians may think of ourselves as superhuman. As physicians in training, we are taught to ignore basic physiologic requirements, such as getting enough sleep, or even eating when we are busy with patient care. At the same time, we want to be the model of health for our patients, but fear that by seeking professional mental health advice we are violating that ideal model.

We also worry that requesting assistance will have an adverse impact on our career—including problems with the state medical board. Medical boards frequently pose ambiguous and scary questions such as, "Have you ever had a medical condition that in any way would or could possibly impact the care you provide for your patients?"

Finally, as a consequence of the long hours they work, physicians put off making time to meet with a mental health professional or even to talk to a friend or colleague. Any additional commitment, even for their own wellbeing, is viewed as a threat or encroachment on their already limited personal time. I experienced this firsthand recently when I suggested to a friend and colleague that we create a burnout support group to meet for an hour once a month. This physician had confided in me about his own symptoms of burnout several times and forwarded me information about the problem. I could feel the panic in his voice when he told me he could not make the time commitment to attend a meeting. I understood and empathized because I had been there myself.

Unfortunately, because of these barriers, by the time a physician finally seeks the help he or she needs, they are often in crisis and they may need emergency psychiatric intervention. At this point, assistance from family and friends who recognize you may be in crisis are a critical resource; don't ignore concern expressed by those close to you—this may be your true wake-up call.

An argument could be made that voluntarily attending a burnout support/prevention meeting, in a casual setting with other physicians in an organization or with a group of smaller clinics, should be a part of every practicing physician's health and wellness program, just like regular appointments are for their patients.

INSTITUTIONAL BARRIERS TO TREATMENT

In addition to treatment barriers at the individual level, many barriers exist in large health care organizations. First, the organization's management must recognize it's a critical and common problem. The larger the organization, the more difficult the recognition process may be.

Beyond recognition, the next step is to develop a plan to address it—usually starting with assigning administrative management of the solutions. In fact the process parallels the steps individual physicians must take to deal with their own burnout; the institution must acknowledge the problem, choose to take action, and then develop a plan to deal with the problems. Each step looks different, the barriers and solutions vary in scale and complexity, and the final results impact not only the physicians themselves but also outcomes for patients, staff, and the organization itself on many levels of health—physical, mental, and financial.

The tipping point may come when the administration realizes the financial health of the organization is threatened by the failure to deal with physician burnout—and a critical institutional barrier can be that the financial threat may not be obvious.

SECTION 2

RECOGNIZING THE CAUSES

CHAPTER 12

WORKING WITH TECHNOLOGY

In the next several chapters we will look at causes and factors that contribute to physician burnout. Understanding the source of the problems is the first step towards finding solutions.

This chapter will focus on how technology can contribute to and exacerbate burnout. Technological advances in imaging and screening tools have without a doubt significantly improved patient care. However, overreliance on technology can also lead to profound depersonalization of the health care we deliver. Other technological changes in the practice of medicine have benefits but also detractors, and if not managed effectively with policy and available resources, can add significantly to a physician's frustration and workload.

ELECTRONIC SCREENING AND IMAGING TOOLS

I have experienced firsthand how using sophisticated imaging techniques as initial screening tools caused a decline in physicians' history-taking and physical exam skills. If a patient presents to an ER with a severe headache, the history and exam of such a patient can be cursory because it is recognized he will get a CT scan of his head. A good history could uncover a potential underlying cause of the headache that may not show up on a CT scan. For example, the patient may have a history of migraines and ate a food that triggered the headache.

Similarly, I witnessed declining cardiac auscultation skills among my colleagues because it was presumed any patient with chest pain or a cardiac complaint would undergo echocardiography or cardiac catheterization. I often feel we are not as adroit in our physical exam skills as previous generations of physicians were, because of our dependence on medical technology, lab work, and imaging. Overreliance on newer electronic testing also robs some of the human connection between patient and physician.

EMR

Electronic medical records systems are an unavoidable requirement in today's medical practice. Many physicians have become frustrated by the use of complex EMR systems written by medically naïve programmers with little to no physician input.

I have learned over twenty different computer systems during my time in practice. At times the practice of medicine was literally dictated by the IT department. For example, during the implementation of a new computer system at one hospital, I was told to decrease my patient load by 70% while administration got the kinks worked out of the new computer system. I literally had patients calling for emergency visits I could not see because of our new computer system. This example is also illustrative of one of the major causes of burnout: a lack of control.

Another time-consuming task in the current healthcare environment is the attempt by hospitals and large organizations to use EMR systems that mandate laborious documentation at each visit to demonstrate compliance with new "meaningful use" requirements created by the Affordable Care Act.

I suspect both providers and patients have experienced office visits where the appointment's purpose seemed secondary in importance to the doctor frantically typing answers into his computer to comply with the standards that must now be met for billing purposes. In the process, we lose the forest for the trees.

PERPETUAL CALL

Smartphones and pagers have increased accessibility to the point that physicians are perpetually on call. The home is no longer a sanctuary, because the hospital can always page or call the physician with patient questions. I personally was called repeatedly in the middle of the night and on weekends. I also received innumerable calls during designated vacation and even on my honeymoon. Every physician has similar stories.

INTERNET MISINFORMATION

Widespread access to the Internet has also increased the number of self-diagnosing patients who, through the power of a Google search, become convinced they have a particular condition or require a certain course of therapy, even if that treatment is in fact the polar opposite of what they need.

PHYSICIAN BURNOUT

I dealt with a remarkable number of patients who, after a search on the Internet, were convinced they had lupus—an autoimmune disorder. These patients erroneously concluded they had lupus because they had symptoms of fatigue, matching one of the multitude of symptoms associated with lupus. Obviously, thousands of conditions can cause fatigue and many of those patients were relieved to learn they did not in fact have lupus. Others, however, were frustrated and questioned my clinical judgment if I told them they did not meet clinical criteria for lupus. They felt they had become experts after a twenty minute Google search. Frequently, patients request unnecessary treatments such as an MRI or specific blood work based on a Google search or something they had seen on Dr. Oz.

PATIENT EMAILS

Direct email access to physicians has resulted in the additional strain of asking overworked, understaffed clinicians to deal with the mass proliferation of emails that now inundate their offices. This can be viewed as another aspect of being on perpetual call. Physicians and staff already have difficulty responding to the forty to fifty phone calls a day the average physician with a full patient panel will receive. Now, they have been further inundated with daily patient emails, many of which contain multiple questions with the expectation of prompt and detailed responses on the part of the physician.

One physician colleague described the new expectation of responding to patient emails as the proverbial straw that broke the camel's back. She originally received two to three emails a day several years ago, but that number has exploded to well over fifty a day. She spends her nights at home answering emails rather than spending time with her two young sons.

CHAPTER 13

UNREALISTIC PATIENT EXPECTATIONS

Many patients have developed inflated or unrealistic expectations from their physicians, including complete recovery from any condition, or at least mitigation of all of their symptoms. Perfection in modern medicine is sometimes obtainable, and in many cases can and should be expected. For example, a patient with gall bladder disease has every right to expect a routine surgical procedure with a normal outcome.

However, in our information age where patients can be swayed by what they read on the Internet or even a Facebook post, they may expect perfection in situations where it may not be attainable. For example, a patient could gain weight as a side effect from a steroid that is vitally needed to control an underlying autoimmune disease. The patient may then become angry at the doctor for this unavoidable weight gain.

Similarly, patients may have had a friend or family member who recovered fully after a complicated intervention such as back surgery, and they assume their outcome should be the same. Patients may measure their treatment by the standard of their own expectations as opposed to what the likely actual medical outcome may be.

I have experienced the consequences of unrealistic patient expectations multiple times and it can exacerbate burnout. I have also had patients become irate when an intervention does not work even though I clearly explained that it would only have a forty to fifty percent chance of success. Sometimes, as human beings, we filter information and conclude that a fifty percent chance of success means this assuredly will work for me—and discount the fact that it's equally likely the intervention will not be effective. Patients and their family members can develop an optimism bias.

As a consequence of the technologic advances that have occurred in medicine over the last thirty years, patients expect that after thorough testing and imaging, all uncertainty can be eliminated and a 100% accurate diagnosis and course of action can be determined. Sometimes, judgment calls still need to be made and some patients are unwilling to accept this.

Patients have a right to receive compassionate care and clear explanations about their condition from physicians who are professional and empathic in their demeanor. However, some patients have unrealistic expectations for an office visit.

I saw many patients who wanted a narcotic prescription for ill-defined back pain the first time I ever saw them. As a rheumatologist, I had patients who asked me to address their cardiac issues, which I clearly was not trained to do. Sometimes, a patient who had seen three or four other specialists would come in with a constellation of symptoms and expect me to make a diagnosis on the spot before I had even seen all their lab work or imaging.

Many patients expect their physician to be accessible twenty-four hours a day, seven days a week. They believe a physician should return their call or respond to their email immediately. My wife, an attorney, is astounded by the fact that medical patients expect a response from their physician in such a timely manner, given the average physician has a panel of about 2,500 patients. She has tried to envision a similar scenario at her law practice where she had 2,500 clients who all expected an immediate and thorough response to their inquiries.

Unrelieved stress can cause a physician to lose perspective. Physicians can significantly worsen their underlying burnout by reacting to unrealistic expectations that patients may have, when a step back from the issue would have saved them from accepting that responsibility.

I have been berated by patients because of the quality of the food they received in the hospital where I worked, clearly something far beyond my control. One of my patient satisfaction and performance scores included feedback from a patient that a receptionist didn't smile enough when he was in my office. On top of the innumerable things I was responsible for, I started to wonder if I needed to address these complaints as well. When we are already at a point where we can't recover from daily stresses, we can't stop the unrealistic expectations some patients bring from affecting us.

Finally, the proliferation of medical rating sites that allow patients to rate their doctors adds another source of stress that, with a healthier perspective, could be taken with a grain of salt. A few disgruntled patients can, and often do, post erroneous information about a doctor, and give their physician a bad grade or rating even though that physician may have acted in a patient's best interest. For example, a physician may refuse to prescribe an opioid drug to a patient with a history of intravenous drug use. That patient may then not only give the doctor a poor review, but also post something malicious or untrue about the physician. The physician has no recourse to respond to unfair accusations, and future potential patients may be swayed by such misinformation.

CHAPTER 14

THE STRESS OF LITIGATION

Have you been injured? Call us at this number! You may be entitled to a reward!

We have all seen these advertisements on TV. Our society has been conditioned to expect 100% successful outcomes—or someone must be at fault. If a patient suffers a known complication from a condition or dies, someone must be held accountable—even if everything was done perfectly from a medical standpoint.

Most American doctors can expect to be sued at some point during their career. I have seen estimates as high as 65% of physicians will be involved in some form of litigation before they retire.[20] The quality and appropriateness of care the physician provides are frequently divorced from the reality of our litigious society. As Ted Epperly pointed out in his book *Fractured,* the United States has approximately 5% of the world's population, yet our country has greater than 50% of the world's lawyers.[21]

The overwhelming majority of lawyers who practice in the United States are not involved in malpractice litigation.

However, the small subset of attorneys specializing in malpractice litigation significantly drive up the cost of healthcare by substantially increasing the practice of defensive medicine. In fact, the cost of defensive medicine has been estimated at an astounding $124 billion per year.[21]

The absolute best physician I know, an internist who trained at Johns Hopkins, recently was sued in a case within my field of rheumatology. This physician made the correct diagnosis and instituted the correct treatment for an incredibly rare condition. The patient suffered a known complication from the condition and elected to sue this doctor. The doctor eventually won the case, but not before being subjected to the psychological and emotional toll of going through a lawsuit.

My father was involved in a frivolous malpractice suit in which the plaintiff who sued him eventually went to prison as a result of the suit when it was revealed the plaintiff who sued him was delinquent on his federal income taxes and child support. My dad obviously won the case. However, he went through an emotional rollercoaster as a result of the trial. Many doctors feel litigation and the threat of being sued is the worst challenge with clinical medicine.

Sometimes doctors look at patients not as human beings going through a difficult time, but as potential adversaries who are going to sue no matter how good their treatment is. Patients are no longer people but rather potential legal liabilities. Our fear of being sued causes us to order more tests, refer to more subspecialists, admit our patients for conservative unnecessary hospitalizations, and generally do more to rule out disease and cover ourselves than we may otherwise.

Fear of lawsuits can result in limited access to treatment for high-risk patients, and for the patients who need subspecialist care. It can lead to over-treatment. The cost of defensive medicine significantly increases the overall cost of healthcare in this country. Many doctors are leaving high risk fields such as obstetrics. For example, my wife's previous gynecologist, who was an outstanding obstetrician, left the practice of obstetrics. It is not unheard of for an obstetrician's medical malpractice premium to cost over $100,000 per year. The fear of being sued has fundamentally changed the doctor-patient relationship and led to mistrust and suspicion on both sides.

A lawsuit is a major life event and physicians suffer drastically when they are sued. When physicians are sued, they can experience intense isolation and embarrassment. It is almost impossible for a physician not to react to a lawsuit as an affront to his ability. Physicians often second-guess their clinical decisions and acumen moving forward after a suit.

Physicians going through a lawsuit experience anxiety and depression and they can understandably obsess over the case that resulted in the suit. Tragically, sometimes physicians who are sued resort to suicide. The ever-looming threat of litigation plays an enormous role in physician burnout, and physicians who are sued are particularly prone to develop severe burnout.

The time for tort reform is long overdue in American medicine. Unfortunately, significant reform was not achieved with the passage of the Affordable Care Act.

Every physician I know can relate a Kafkaesque tale about medical litigation involving themselves or a colleague. Physicians want patients who are injured as a result of medical error or negligence to be justly compensated. However, the current system does not adequately ensure that this happens. Instead, excess litigation drives up the cost of care because of defensive medicine.

If we do not achieve significant tort reform, medicine will be a less palatable career choice for the best and brightest of the next generation. We are already rapidly losing doctors in high risk subspecialties as a consequence of our current litigation system. In what other profession do aspiring trainees know their chances of being sued are better than 50%, over the course of their careers?

CHAPTER 15

OVERBOOKED SCHEDULES

Due to patient volume and time constraints, physicians at many institutions are like gerbils on a spinning wheel. They see more patients than they did in the 1960s and 70s, and have significantly more administrative tasks to perform for each patient visit outside the exam room, compared to prior eras in medicine. As pointed out by Dr. Sandeep Jahur, in an editorial in the Wall Street Journal, the 1970 average inflation adjusted annual salary of a general practitioner was $185,000 compared to a figure of $161,000 in 2010. Yet, the general practitioner of 2010 sees nearly double the number of patients per day compared to his 1970 predecessor.[22]

A tightly packed patient schedule can demoralize many physicians, and the proverbial "seven minute visit" limits their ability to provide the quality care they want to give their patients.

This problem is expected to worsen, as over thirty million new and previously uninsured patients flood the healthcare system with the passage of the Affordable Care Act. And, to compound the problem even further, the baby boom population is aging and developing the sequelae of age-associated medical conditions such as heart disease, osteoporosis and Alzheimer's disease. Overscheduled doctors are dealing with both an influx of new patients while grappling with sicker ones already under their care.

Patients grasp the severity of this issue when they must wait four months for an appointment. My mother called for a semi-urgent rheumatologic evaluation and got an appointment for six weeks later. She was surprised by how long it took, whereas I was surprised by how quickly she got in, given the subspecialist shortage in this area.

When I was suffering from burnout, I felt burdened by an overbooked schedule. This is a common symptom. There are too many patients to see and not enough hours in the day. In today's healthcare system, physicians frequently are compensated based on the volume of patients they see. A higher patient volume per day results in less time per patient, and consequently, the quality of care declines.

A recently released survey by the RAND Corporation demonstrated that the ability to deliver high quality care to patients was associated with physician satisfaction.[23] Based on my own experience and information from numerous physicians, an overloaded physician who can't provide adequate care will become demoralized, which can severely exacerbate burnout.

Physicians become accustomed to running at an artificially fast pace starting in medical residency, and we think it is normal to do so for the rest of our careers. As an analogy, I have a treadmill at home with a top speed of ten miles an hour. When I jog on it, I would never think of going over seven miles an hour for any length of time. Compared to my patient schedule, my comfortable treadmill pace would have been to see about fourteen to seventeen patients a day. Yet I consistently saw patients in the mid-thirty range (or analogously ran a treadmill pace of over ten miles an hour) all day long. In today's environment, physicians commonly see forty or fifty patients a day in an outpatient clinic.

It is impossible to practice good medicine at this pace. One of my mentors, Dr. Fu, repeatedly admonished me, "Dr. Murphy, you can never do a good job in medicine when you are rushing!" In her book *What Doctors Feel*, Danielle Ofri, an internist, encapsulated this sentiment when she described her experience of overseeing the management of forty-plus patients at New York's Bellevue Hospital: "I was practicing substandard medicine and I knew it."[24]

Patients are not pleased with "speed" medicine either. As a patient, I have literally rehearsed what I wanted to say to the physician before he entered the room, because I intuitively knew I would have about two minutes to get everything out. I could identify, and I understood his predicament. I had been there myself.

Occasionally a healthy patient will come in for a prescription refill that can be accomplished in a short period of time, but physicians try to use this same model for more complex, older patients with multiple medical problems. It is not possible to conduct a thorough history, physical exam, review lab work, formulate a treatment plan, and answer all questions a complex patient may have in ten minutes, but physicians will try because they are way behind schedule.

At the end of the day, demoralized by these interactions, they wonder if they missed something because they were in survival mode all day. The data, what other physicians have shared with me, and my personal experience all confirm that physicians are working long, stressful hours and at a more frenetic pace than was required in prior eras. As a result, we are unable to deliver thorough and attentive care that makes us feel good about our job.

I know many physicians who are perpetually running behind schedule or working through lunch, in an attempt to catch up from the morning schedule. When I reached my point of maximum burnout, I would arrive at work in the morning, look at my daily schedule and feel completely overwhelmed. How could I possibly get through the day?

It is time to take a step back and acknowledge that we are not superhuman and to bring some sanity back into our schedule. This may mean a reduction in patient volume for many physicians who are suffering from burnout. Taking this step likely will mean a decrease in a physician's current salary, but it can have long lasting, positive impacts on quality of life.

Unfortunately, the current compensation scheme in this country does not recognize the vital importance of physicians in our society. We are compensated on volume and speed and this can result in poorer outcomes, with both lower physician and patient satisfaction. At the end of the day, it will be up to physicians to choose how they want to practice. In my experience, less is often more.

CHAPTER 16

CALL SCHEDULES AND SCOPE OF PRACTICE

Unfortunately, perhaps more so than other professions, being on call in medicine is synonymous with working. And unlike many professions, most doctors are not compensated for being on call.

Patients obviously do not adhere to a nine-to-five schedule when they get sick, injure themselves, or break a bone. They come in for help on holidays, late at night, or early in the morning. One weekend in Wisconsin, I was called to see a hospitalized patient during a white out blizzard. I barely made it to the hospital, spent several hours there and upon my return home, as I was walking through the door, another physician called with another rheumatologic emergency, and I was forced to go back to the hospital. All physicians who have taken call have similar stories. Interns and residents routinely spend the night in the hospital taking call.

I also was called many times when I wasn't on call. This is a common experience for many doctors. I was called at night, while on vacation, even on my honeymoon. I also was called at night by other doctors for non-urgent referrals to my clinic. I did not establish boundaries and my family life suffered as a consequence.

One difficult situation that almost all physicians are familiar with is the narcotic-seeking patient who requests a refill for a strong narcotic, such as Oxycontin, over the weekend. If the doctor fills the prescription, he may be helping a drug addict score a fix. If he refuses, the patient may make a formal complaint with the hospital and the physician could be reprimanded for not treating the patient's pain. This situation could be avoided by instituting a policy that requires the patient be seen by the prescribing physician for any narcotic or habit-forming drug. This is reasonable and protects not only the on-call physician but the patients themselves.

For all of these reasons, call can have a demoralizing impact and is a source of burnout. Second only to the daily stress of an overloaded patient schedule, a physician's call schedule causes a critical loss of control, autonomy, and quality of life while away from work. An emergency can crop up at any time. If a physician goes out to dinner, he or she may not have a glass of wine because of their call schedule. A physician may be anticipating or dreading the pager going off when spending time with his or her family on the weekend. Even if the pager does not actually go off, it theoretically could and this has significant quality of life implications.

Post-call exhaustion is another complication. If I was at the hospital late, my next day's patients were at risk, as I would show up for work fatigued. I also suffered from an anticipatory pre-call anxiety. For days leading up to call I was stressed. I first observed this phenomenon growing up with my father prior to his calls.

CHAPTER 16

When I shared call with a group, it was incredibly stressful when a patient with a complex medical history called me, and I was expected to render a clinical judgment without having met the patient or even seen their medication list and labs.

Treating an unknown patient over the phone can cause serious complications, and increase both the potential for errors and risk of litigation. While on call, you are responsible for any advice you give. If the outcome is bad, you are fully legally liable. A diabetic patient of mine received a course of steroids to treat a gout attack from an on-call physician. The patient's blood sugars went up as result of the steroids and he had to be admitted to the hospital.

Call duty may inadvertently include treating conditions outside your scope of expertise, also increasing the odds for errors and litigation. Set boundaries by clearly defining both your scope and your call schedule, to protect the patients and yourself.

CHAPTER 17

MEDICINE HAS CHANGED

Medicine has always been a challenging job. However, compared to fifty years ago, the fulfillment my grandfather experienced seems unattainable, given the harsh realities imposed by the bureaucracy, litigiousness, and financial pressures that confront the profession today.

Many of the changes have been positive. Technological and scientific advances in medicine and treatment options have radically improved American medicine. As a result, many diseases and injuries can be healed in apparently miraculous ways. The sophisticated imaging techniques, improved understanding of the immune system, and other medical advances have resulted in the public's perception that any condition is fixable. Unfortunately, this is not the case. Some diseases have no cure; some conditions cause serious health complications that the patient must learn to live with; and some patients will die prematurely. The modern-day physician must be the bearer of bad news, when no drug or treatment exists to repair the damage done by a disease or injury. Some patients don't understand this reality, or refuse to face it. And some will blame the physician who could not fix their health issues.

Many patients simply don't trust the clinical judgment of their physician if it is discordant with something they have read online or on social media. One time, when I tried to reassure a patient about a false positive blood test, she replied, "I read online you would say that, and not to believe you if you did."

While technological and medical advances have occurred at a rapid pace, the profession of medicine itself has completely transformed as well, and many physicians believe it has changed for the worse. Schedules are completely overbooked with patients, more so than in the past, while physicians are simultaneously inundated with paperwork and administrative tasks.

I recently attended the funeral of my Uncle Tom, a skilled heart surgeon, who practiced medicine the way he wanted to. He was unafraid to tell patients or hospital administrators what he thought, no matter how politically incorrect. During the ceremony, physician relatives repeatedly said Tom would never have been able to practice his way in the modern medical environment. Other physician relatives in their sixties confided they were very relieved they either had retired—or were in the process of retiring—from the practice of medicine. One relative expressed sadness and concern that his daughter had elected to go into medicine.

Today, doctors simply don't have the time to inquire about someone's granddaughter or talk about the upcoming season's little league prospects with a patient who is a coach.

While in the past many physicians ran their own clinics, today they are slowly losing any measure of autonomy over their practice as medicine moves towards the employment model. My grandfather saw the number of patients he felt was clinically appropriate, while in our current system physicians are trying to meet productivity and volume-driven goals.

A recent study by the RAND Corporation found a significant component in physician satisfaction is the importance of autonomy in making medical decisions for their patients.[25] My grandfather practiced in such a fashion. My dad started to lose some of his autonomy when he practiced and I certainly was acutely aware of that loss with the encroachment of government mandates and regulation, as well as the hurdles created by insurance companies.

Physicians of a prior era were not buried in the morass of paperwork that engulfs us now. My grandfather never had to hunch over a computer screen clicking off boxes to satisfy an insurance mandate for billing purposes, or satisfy criteria for "meaningful use." Most physicians were not at the mercy of a bureaucratic system and they charged a fee for the service they provided. They were compensated by patients directly before the insurance industry entered the picture. Doctors were viewed as benefactors of the community and were well respected. Physicians were generally content with this system, as was my grandfather and his brother who both practiced during the halcyon days of a bygone era in the forties and fifties.

In prior eras, a physician kept up with advances in medicine out of his own desire to be a good physician. Today, physicians are required to leap through bureaucratic hoops to ensure they are compliant with a labyrinth of regulations, such as maintenance of certification, that define modern medicine.

The bureaucracy and paperwork in modern medicine almost seems like a beast that feeds itself in a self-sustaining loop. It continues to grow exponentially and out of control, seriously contributing to physician burnout. When my grandfather and father went into medicine, they underwent the arduous task of medical training so they could help people, as opposed to becoming glorified claims processers for the health insurance industry.

More responsibility is piled on as we are asked to fill out hospital compliance modules or learn new EMR systems on our personal time, all while we are expected to keep up to date with the latest medical advances and readings. Simultaneously, we must study to remain board certified and maintain certification in our specialty.

Trust and respect for physicians has tangibly eroded amongst the general public. Many physicians feel they get little respect from some of the patients they care for and the hospital administrators they work for.

No wonder morale is so low in the medical community now. In a 2008 survey by the Physician's Foundation of 12,000 physicians, only 6% characterized their morale as positive.[26] A physician relative recently told me, "I never would have gone into the profession today. It's gotten so bad that at my office I have three medical assistants; two of them do paperwork full time and don't do anything medically related. Only one of them actually assists me in day-to-day interactions, taking care of patients." Another physician in his eighties told me, "The profession does not remotely resemble the profession I entered into fifty years ago. My daughter has left the practice of medicine altogether in her mid-thirties and I am glad she did." No wonder a survey in 2012, of 5,000 physicians by the Doctor's Company, showed that nine out of ten doctors would not recommend the profession to others.[27]

SECTION 3

SOLUTIONS TO BURNOUT

CHAPTER 18

MAKING THE DECISION YOU ARE GOING TO DO SOMETHING

Start close in, don't take the second step or the third, start with the first thing close in, the step you don't want to take.

Poem: David Whyte

Without change or intervention, burnout will almost inevitably spiral into a maladaptive lifestyle resulting in the serious adverse effects mentioned in previous chapters.

RECOGNITION

The first and largest step is to acknowledge the problem exists. This is particularly difficult because one of the first things a physician suffering from burnout sheds is a regard for his or her own wellbeing. The physician in this predicament has frequently become so cynical, jaded, and worn down that he or she is unwilling to commit to his or her own health.

My wife summarized this sentiment: "You would never allow another person to treat me with malicious contempt and a complete lack of regard for my wellbeing. Yet, you live and treat yourself this way every day."

We can become creatures of habit and unconsciously choose to live in an unhappy environment. We cede control of our lives to our schedule, to the existing parameters we can't seem to control. Our life becomes automatic, preordained. Life will be good when we finally save enough money to retire, and until then we reconcile ourselves to simply existing in survival mode. We defer our very lives and our dreams. We delude ourselves by saying things have changed and we have new priorities, and those old hopes and aspirations did not really matter. Yet, there is a nagging ache within our heart that tells us something is amiss.

I have met many physicians who are miserable; they feel they made a bad choice in choosing medicine, but are willing to consign themselves to a life of diminished expectations. They have confided in me that it is too late, that they feel powerless and "stuck." However, they are not. Choosing to get better is always an option.

SOMETHING HAS TO GIVE: ACKNOWLEDGING CHANGE

The second step is realizing change and action must accompany the acknowledgement of burnout. I have met a number of physicians who get to the acknowledgement stage but cannot proceed any further. Some physicians locked in this stage get stuck in a quicksand of frustration and anger, where they simply want to go to a medical website dedicated to physicians, such as Sermo (sermo.com), and try to find a blog or article about how terrible the state of American medicine is for practicing physicians.

CHAPTER 18

CHOOSE TO ACT

You have to choose to act. I think it is very helpful to realize you are not alone—but nothing will change until you decide it must. Otherwise you will be reading the same angry blogs and web posts five years from now. I have been there, and fell into that victim role.

Physicians who don't acknowledge they must change are choosing not to choose. They are relegating themselves to a life of unhappiness, and are unwilling to make the necessary changes to improve their current situation. Ironically, by not deciding to actively do something, these physicians are letting the system and circumstances that made them unhappy continue to dominate their lives.

The only way to get out of burnout is to acknowledge the problem and resolve to do something about it. The recognition, acknowledgement, and commitment to do something are the biggest hurdles in its treatment. Once you take these steps and recognize burnout for the professional emergency that it is, you are on the road to recovery.

When making this decision, it is imperative to put yourself and your family first—above coworkers, the hospital, and even patients. Although this may seem selfish, it is essential you regain some measure of autonomy. Otherwise you are consigning yourself to a lifetime of reluctantly working for others while denying yourself the chance to enjoy life.

When a physician makes the decision to do something about burnout, it is like screaming "eureka!" Suddenly, a vast new world of possibility exists and a burden feels like it's lifted from his or her shoulders.

CHAPTER 19

BE COMMITTED TO THE CHANGE

Change must occur to truly begin recovery from burnout. Simply reading this book will not suffice. You must implement changes and commit to those changes, meaning it will cost you time and effort.

Change and commitment are hard even under ideal circumstances. Obviously, committing to time-consuming and difficult changes will be extremely challenging for an overworked, stressed, and overscheduled person. However, once you acknowledge the need and make the commitment, the hardest part of the voyage is over.

In order to reinforce the importance of acknowledging and committing to making changes, I have included a contract at the end of this chapter. If you are willing to make the commitment, I am asking you to sign and date it, and give a copy to your spouse or other important person who will be willing to hold you accountable.

IDENTIFY YOUR CRITICAL CHANGES

Before you can make changes, you must know what to change. Rank those aspects of your professional life most in need of improvement. The previous chapter on contributing factors can serve as a starting point for identification. Then, the following chapters describe solutions that worked for me and others. Select those you feel most applicable to your situation and commit to follow them through. Enlist a trusted person, such as a spouse, to support your decisions and help you stick to your goals. Revisit the contract you made with yourself every several weeks.

Your life is about to change. It will not be easy, but soon your life can be much better and your family, the organization where you work, and your patients will be glad you made the change.

STICK TO IT

Now comes the tricky part: you must be true to yourself and stick to your resolve. You have everything to gain.

Clearly communicate to your partners or the organization where you work that you are making these changes, and work out a designated time period for implementation. Emphasize that the changes are non-negotiable and necessary for your personal health and wellbeing.

IMPLEMENT CHANGES

Work to implement your changes, and transform your working environment and your life. This will involve commitment of time and energy—but once you make the commitment, you will have gained a measure of control over your life and wellbeing that you didn't have before.

It is vital to enlist support and make others aware of the changes you plan to implement. Once others are aware you are making these changes, it introduces an additional level of accountability. Other people will monitor your actions to see if you are keeping your commitment, and many will help you.

FIND WHAT WORKS FOR YOU

After releasing data documenting the "alarming" rate of physician burnout in a landmark study in The Archives of Internal Medicine, the authors of the study concluded that little available evidence exists on how best to address and treat this problem.[28]

The good news is that a multitude of interventions can work. I have come to the conclusion that no single algorithm or work plan can be used to treat all physicians suffering from burnout. Each individual physician will have to choose amongst several lifestyle and workplace changes and find what works for him or her in order to achieve success. This is a rapidly evolving field—and I am amazed and heartened to see the multitude of interventions that are developed literally by the day.

In the following chapters, we will focus on specific changes you can make once you have acknowledged the problem, identified those areas to change, and committed to change. As we will see, strategies and treatment options lag behind the growing professional and larger societal recognition of the problem of physician burnout.

COMMITMENT CONTRACT

Below is a contract template that I recommend you personalize, sign and date, and share with another trusted person close to you. That person can help you remain committed to the program.

Before you are ready to sign this contract, make a list of those aspects of your job that must change to improve your quality of life. Here are some examples.

1. I will commit to taking three weeks of vacation a year.
2. I will notify my office and hospital system that I am going to work one less day a week and cut down on my daily patient volumes.
3. I will delegate more responsibility to my office staff, and ask them to screen and review emails I get from patients.
4. I will see a counselor to discuss my feelings of burnout.

CHAPTER 19

PERSONAL COMMITMENT CONTRACT

I, _____,
enter into this contract with myself and family on this _____
day of _____, _____ to improve my personal wellbeing
and that of my family.

I acknowledge that I am experiencing signs and symptoms consistent with burnout. I also acknowledge that professional burnout has had a negative impact on my job and my personal life.

I commit to changing aspects of my job and life so I can begin to heal myself, realizing this will not always be easy. That change begins today with my signature of this contract.

I will implement the following changes immediately to begin my recovery:

1.
2.
3.
4.

I have an accountability partner (name of spouse, partner, friend, or family member): _____
who witnesses this contract and who will measure my progress and commitment to change. The signature of my accountability partner:_____Date:_____

I will sit down with my accountability partner at least once a month to measure my progress and commitment to the behavioral changes I have identified.

Signed, _____Date:_____

CHAPTER 20

SEEK PEER SUPPORT AND COUNSELING

PEER SUPPORT NETWORK AND SPONSORSHIP

There is an old saying in medical school about how physicians learn to do procedures, such as spinal taps: "See one. Do one. Teach one." I believe a major component of my recovery from burnout came from talking with other physicians who had gone through this process. Support models such as Alcoholics Anonymous serve for what I think will work for physician burnout.

I was extremely lucky to have two physicians, who I would categorize as sponsors, help me through the process of burnout recovery. On a human level, knowing you are not the only one struggling with this problem, and hearing about strategies other people have used can be tremendously encouraging. I have served in a mentor/sponsor capacity myself. At Heal Thyself MD (tommurphymd.com), we are in the beginning stages of looking at these models and putting them in place. We plan on using them as one of the foundations of our long term treatment plan.

When a physician functions as a sponsor, it further enhances his or her own recovery as it enables the physician sponsor to continue to be mindful of the practice of the life-changing techniques that resulted in his or her recovery. Unfortunately, I have not uncovered any studies about the use of physician sponsorship or mentors as a way of treating burnout, but such a study is one of the many goals we wish to undertake as a component of the ten year plan at Heal Thyself MD.

I strongly encourage physicians to look into the option of local physician peer groups, whether through a physician wellness committee at a local hospital or setting up a group of friends and colleagues. An additional potential resource may be The Heart of Medicine website (http://theheartofmedicine. org/), where physicians can evaluate potential local support options. The main point is to get into a group and talk about what is going on. It is pivotal for the recovery process.

COUNSELING

Many physicians going through burnout recovery would benefit from further support outside of their immediate family, friends, and peers. Counseling through a psychologist, psychiatrist, or employee assistance program can be of great benefit. Psychiatrist Don Jacobson, a burnout expert, expressed his concern to me that some physicians were not seeking help for burnout because doing so meant the problem was intrinsic to them and their inability to cope with the situation.

Seeking help, especially including psychiatric counseling, can be a healthy, vital part of the recovery process. As a community, physicians need to work to destigmatize the option of seeking psychiatric care for physicians. Similarly, hospital administrations need to support these efforts, and large health care systems should try to provide a psychiatrist or psychologist who has experience in the area of burnout management. I know of one large healthcare organization that employs such a model, which will be discussed further in a future chapter.

In addition to burnout, if a physician is suffering coexisting depression, it is imperative for him or her to seek psychiatric care. Burnout and depression are a highly toxic and potentially lethal mix. I am aware of three physician acquaintances who suffered from this combination and all three ended their own lives.

CHAPTER 21

REESTABLISH YOUR FINANCIAL GOALS

Many doctors I know who are suffering from burnout are in a financially precarious position. A recent survey showed that only 17% of physicians rated the financial standing of their practice as "healthy and profitable."[29] One of the keys to formulating a long term plan for burnout management is to first reestablish a firm financial base with a well-thought-out plan for the future.

A financial advisor may be beneficial in this situation. At Heal Thyself MD, I partner with Dr. Cory S. Fawcett, a surgeon, who is now working with physicians as they formulate a financial plan for their future. You can learn more about how Cory is helping other physicians at tommurphymd.com. It is imperative to develop a long term strategy for retirement savings, debt reduction, and children's college funds—whether you use a financial advisor or not

If you do not have a long term strategy for these scenarios, you have relinquished control of your future—and you may feel you are treading water just to stay afloat.

I know many physicians who have no savings and no financial cushion. For example, I know physicians who regularly use their credit card to make a monthly car payment and who make the minimum payment on credit card bills when they come due. I even know some physician acquaintances that have fallen victim to investment scams. Other physicians I have met made risky real estate investments before the bubble burst. I know many physicians that simply are not very good with money. They are accomplished and intelligent, and are reluctant to admit they need help, or to take the time and effort to develop a comprehensive strategy for the management of their finances.

Divorce or illness will compound financial problems. And some physicians simply live above their means. We all are aware of the physicians who drive the fancy imported European sports car, take lavish vacations, and own a yacht or a million dollar home. I do not begrudge people the right to any of these luxuries, but if taken too far, they often can tragically result in the accumulation of significant debt.

In many cases, these situations can be controlled with several simple steps. These include setting financial goals, creating a budget, and finally, just getting organized. These can seem like monolithic tasks to a burned out physician, but they must be a priority and they are essential components to getting your life back in order. Like a commitment to a diet or exercise program, developing a sound financial strategy and sticking to your goals requires a fair amount of discipline and may entail some sacrifices.

The first step on the road to financial independence is to determine exactly how much you owe and structure a sensible payment plan. Learning about basic investing and money management, although it may seem daunting, is very doable.

I was definitely naïve in this realm. I literally knew nothing, but once I learned about basic financial management I was able to resolve debt, set money aside, and create a financial cushion. If I can do it, believe me, anybody can do it. My dad invested wisely and when he saw a change in the direction of medicine he found unpalatable, he was able to retire in his fifties.

When you get your financial house in order, it creates a freedom that allows you to live the life you want on your terms. Retirement becomes a real, definitive goal. It will allow you to practice medicine the way you wish to, because that is how you want to occupy your time, rather than something you must do just to remain solvent. Your joy in the medical profession will be enhanced when you do it because you want to, instead of being a slave to your job to survive financially.

CHAPTER 22

YOU CAN'T BE ALL THINGS TO ALL PEOPLE

Physicians who always say yes can significantly exacerbate burnout. In general, our culture has conditioned us to take on additional responsibilities or favors when asked, and this is particularly true in the medical community.

For example another physician requests a colleague see a patient the same day or at least overbook them on the colleague's schedule that week. A hospital administrator may request a physician provide additional backup call for a colleague at the last minute. Perhaps partly because our medical training schooled us to always accommodate extra requests, physicians agree, when internally they are screaming no.

For example, a hospital administrator once requested I help an internal medicine doctor on vacation, who was an anti-coagulation specialist. This specialist's call schedule was not covered for the week he was out of town. I very reluctantly agreed to the request, and almost instantaneously calls started flooding in. They included very specific questions about anti-coagulation regiments predicated on lab work, and I immediately recognized I was in way over my head. It would have been clinically inappropriate for me to attempt to manage these calls. And worse, I was so overwhelmed trying to accommodate them that it detracted from my ability to manage the patients in my own clinic. I immediately called the administrator and explained the situation and he found another physician more suited for the task. Furthermore, the administrator apologized for the inconvenience.

We, as physicians, operate under the misguided assumption that we can do it all, 100% of the time. That extra task or responsibility we can't turn down adds to the sense of overwhelming burden. We have to learn to politely say no—and we can do it in many ways.

I recommend physicians have answers ready when the inevitable questions arise. Here are some examples:

1. Can you fit that patient in today?

    "I am really sorry but I cannot. My schedule is already at the capacity I feel comfortable with. My office will get them in at the earliest possible time. We will also put them on our cancellation list in case an opening comes up before their scheduled time. Thank you for your understanding, and we look forward to seeing your patient soon."

2. Can you cover my call this weekend?

    If this is something you would prefer not to do, answer with a truthful statement. For example, if you had planned something as simple as spending time with your family, respond to the request by saying you already have made plans with your family—and don't feel guilty about saying no.

"I am sorry but I already made plans with my family this weekend. I am always happy to switch call schedules and do favors when we can work it out in advance, but since we already have plans I cannot cover your call."

Learn to politely and firmly say no. This is a skill. Frequently we overestimate what the cost of saying no will mean. It does not make us "bad" or "weak" to say no. Be firm and not overly apologetic and certainly not defensive when you say no. Saying, "It doesn't fit in my schedule" is acceptable and if someone persists in asking for a favor they are being rude. Also, you don't owe anyone a detailed explanation when you are saying no. This is your right.

There are only so many hours in a day and each time you say yes to one more favor, you have assumed a new commitment you must squeeze into your schedule. This will severely impact your ability to do other things, including self-care priorities like exercising or spending time with your family.

If what you are agreeing to is less important than these other activities, then you really don't have time in your schedule. You need to learn to say no at these times. In learning to say no, you will significantly reduce your stress level. You will be performing an enormous act of kindness to yourself and your family, and giving yourself more time to focus on the task at hand or get home earlier from work.

CHAPTER 23

CREATE BOUNDARIES THAT ALLOW YOU TO LOVE YOUR WORK

Physicians may see more patients in a day than is appropriate for either the physician or the patients. Here are some tips for structuring your day and determining patient volume.

SCHEDULING GROUND RULES

Concerning patient scheduling, I believe it is imperative to establish some ground rules. I say this after analyzing my own behavior and speaking with many physicians about this topic. It is vital to have forty-five minutes to an hour every day devoted to lunch time. Think of this as sanctuary: a time free from work responsibility. This is time when you can stop, catch your breath, and recharge for the afternoon. You can leave the hospital or office and have lunch with a spouse or friend, use onsite exercise facilities, or simply take a walk.

My own sanctuaries included breakfast with my family and making sure I was always home for dinner by 5:30, every day. I also carved out half a day a week as time I would not see patients, but instead could catch up on paperwork and the administrative tasks that come with a medical practice.

MANAGING PATIENT VOLUME

In terms of patient volume, I recommend the following general rules:

1. Set caps on the number of patients you see each day. Decide what works for you and don't compare yourself to others. If your comfort zone is fifteen patients a day while a partner's is twenty-five, that is irrelevant to you. Choose a number that allows you to provide a solid level of care you can feel good about, and can do without feeling rushed or overwhelmed.

2. Assess the parameters and lengths of your visits. Do you have thirty minutes for a new patient visit when in fact you need an hour or at least forty-five minutes? Are your patient follow-up visits only ten minutes when they need to be twenty or thirty minutes?

3. Develop and stick to your policy about late visits and patient no-shows. If a patient shows up an hour late and it will adversely impact your schedule, have the patient reschedule rather than allow it to impact your ability to see other patients or interfere with your lunch break. All too often we "cram" these patients in, short-changing other patients and ourselves.

4. Build two 15-minute breaks into your schedule, one in the morning and one after noon. Use them to catch up if you are behind or look forward to who is next—or check labs, make some patient phone calls, or contact a specialist you need for a patient consultation. When things go smoothly, use this time to recharge and meditate, relax, or make a personal phone call. You also have the option to slot in a patient who needs to be seen semi-emergently.

REDUCING WORK WEEK

One physician friend who was suffering from significant burnout found that reducing the number of work days per week from five to three changed his life. Determine how many days a week you can healthfully and effectively practice the type of medicine you aspire to. That may mean you work four days a week, or three and a half, or two, but determine a number that feels right to you. Write that number down and talk it over with your spouse or other important person in your life.

REDUCING YOUR PATIENT PANEL

If your patient panel is too large, write a letter to your patients explaining the situation to them. Include introductions to alternative physicians in your group. Close your practice to new patients. If your panel is already overloaded and you continue to accept new patients, you are hurting not only yourself, but also showing disrespect to your current patients by limiting their access to care.

By saying yes to everyone, you develop a victim mentality and in the process prevent yourself from providing an optimal level of care. An overloaded panel also leads to increased patient wait times, which can increase stress and patient phone calls, emails, and complaints. It will become increasingly difficult to handle the increased call volume and respond to emails. Your patients may become impatient and switch to another provider, and significant resources will be devoted to triaging phone calls and trying to determine priority patients. Finally, an overwhelming patient load leads to discontinuity and disjointed care, making obtaining appointments and follow-ups more difficult.

CHAPTER 24

MANAGE AND MODIFY CALL SCHEDULE

One of the most important aspects of a physician's obligation is call. When you are on call, you have to take what comes without warning, and you will be contacted about any emergency or need that arises in your specialty during your watch. The most important aspect of managing call is maintaining a clear line of communication, and defining "on" and "off" times. I would strongly recommend never allowing hazy or poorly defined gray areas. Clarify very early on what the exact specifications of a call schedule are.

CLEARLY DEFINE ON AND OFF TIMES

I have been called on the day before my wedding, during my honeymoon, and on vacations—and each time the situation was very frustrating because these were supposed to be designated time off. These intrusive aggravations can drastically worsen underlying burnout, and I definitely felt they exacerbated mine.

If your call week is very high-volume or stressful with multiple emergent situations, you may want to consider reducing your call schedule frequency—if that is a possibility. If you are the only specialist working for a hospital organization, you may want to negotiate an arrangement restricting your accessibility to certain hours during certain days, as I eventually did. If a rheumatologic emergency occurred during the hours I was not on call, the situation was managed by the hospitalist service at our institution.

ESTABLISH OTHER BOUNDARIES

Establish boundaries with other physicians in your group when you are on call. Some physicians try to "backdoor" their way out of call responsibilities. For example, one physician in a shared call group would surreptitiously schedule patients he had been called about onto my schedule, or when he was called by a hospital in the area he would instruct the physician calling to just contact me instead, because I was physically closer. Finally, I convened a meeting to address the issue directly, and all the other members of the call group sided with me.

Be clear about the scope of your practice, and what specialty areas it is clinically appropriate for you to cover.

If you clearly define and set limits and boundaries on your call expectations, and what constitutes an acceptable call schedule, it will markedly improve your professional life. Due to the myriad of other stressors associated with practicing medicine, I am a strong advocate for limiting your call responsibilities and your time on call as much as possible.

CHAPTER 25

DEVELOP STRATEGIES FOR EFFECTIVE USE OF EMR

Dealing with the demands of electronic medical record systems can be a source of frustration and can exacerbate burnout. Many physicians view EMR as another roadblock that prevents them from providing optimal care for their patients. They feel the laptop is coming between them and their patients, and the increasing use of computers is solely about financial remuneration. But whether physicians like it or not, EMR systems will be a part of the landscape of modern medicine.

DELEGATE THE SIMPLE STUFF

I have found several ways to deal with EMR systems. First, delegate whenever you can. Don't waste time and energy on tasks that don't require a medical degree or training. Medical office assistants can be of great help in data entry and other work where appropriate.

A medical scribe can also dramatically reduce your time spent charting. The scribe enters the pertinent information during the physician/patient encounter. This frees you from the data entry task, and can significantly improve your morale as well as increase patient satisfaction. Your office visit time is spent actually interacting with the patient, instead of hiding behind a computer screen.

LEARN THE SYSTEM

Next, learn how to use the systems' strengths in retrieving patient history and data. In one case, I spent unnecessary time and energy bemoaning a major electronic record transition that was implemented. Finally, when I accepted the fact that the new EMR system was here to stay, I sought out the most adroit users of the system at my workplace. These superstars were able to provide me with invaluable tips, which dramatically improved the quality of my workday.

I then asked to work directly with the EMR vendor's IT support staff, who showed me short cuts and features that actually improved patient care. I also accessed online help from the EMR vendor. From that moment on, before I ever started work at a new hospital, I made sure I was up to date and proficient with the EMR system I would be using. Once I mastered each system, I even came to appreciate their benefits—namely the quick accessibility they afforded to patients' labs and radiography, and even treatment guidelines for some conditions.

Health organizations can also significantly aid the implementation of EMR systems by identifying computer skills physicians will need, and providing access to training and learning resources, to make the transition as smooth as possible. Additionally, health organizations should designate enthusiastic "super users" who are willing to teach others. EMR system training for physicians should focus on areas they will use—and limit or eliminate time spent on optional parts of the system. Focused assistance and training can prevent wasted time and added frustration for already overburdened physicians.

POST-IMPLEMENTATION REVIEW

Every hospital organization should conduct a post implementation review for any new EMR system. Every EMR system has snags and flaws, and it is imperative to find them and resolve them as soon as possible. Hospital administration should facilitate error checking, and also poll different departments about what their experience has been with the system and what areas need improvement. Preferably, a physician representative or several of them should be designated to interact with other physicians to gain feedback about the system and to provide accountability that problem areas will be addressed.

CHAPTER 26

TAKE CONTROL OF WORKPLACE ENVIRONMENT

The next area to take control over is your working environment. Don't accept working in a chaotic or dysfunctional environment. Medicine is fundamentally stressful, and working in a difficult environment can make it unbearable.

OFFICE STAFF

I have encountered instances of problematic ancillary staff, nurses, and medical office assistants. If absenteeism, poor attitude, hostility, or passive-aggressive behavior is impacting your work day, communicate with the involved party about the situation in a calm and respectful tone. This often results in improvement in the situation without any need for further intervention.

For example, I had an otherwise outstanding receptionist who understood my policy requiring patients more than thirty minutes late to reschedule their appointment. Yet, she would interrupt me in an exam room and sometimes beseeched me to see late patients. When we sat down to discuss the situation, she explained that it was difficult to turn patients away and they sometimes became angry or hostile. I acknowledged the difficulty of these interactions, and then gave her examples of how this policy was necessary and how an attempt to accommodate late patients had a lasting negative impact on the rest of my schedule and day. Her behavior changed and the issue was resolved.

Sometimes an initial conversation doesn't work, and subsequent steps must be taken. In one instance, the physicians at one clinic had an issue with a support staff member's behavior. We discussed the issue with her on several occasions. She did not respond after repeated interventions, so we let her go. Although this was a difficult and unfortunate circumstance, it immediately improved the working environment and morale of the other staff.

STANDARDIZED PROCEDURES

The way individuals respond to the demands of high stress jobs is very much a reflection of their ability to influence and control their work environment. The stress response is amplified if the individual is powerless to change inefficient, disruptive, or incorrect processes.

The use of standard protocols and order sets were developed in health organizations to streamline common procedures. However, if a standard protocol is controversial, outdated, or bypasses critical control processes, it can be an impediment to appropriate patient care.

For example, a physician recently told me that a standard order form for back pain at the institution where he worked required the patient to receive around-the-clock narcotic doses and an MRI of the spine. Many physicians would question the merits of such a treatment plan.

In another example, I know of a hospitalist who became frustrated one busy night when he was paged by a nurse to clarify admission orders for a patient he had not yet heard about, much less seen. His organization had recently instituted a policy allowing ER physicians to admit a patient to the hospital directly and write "wrap around" orders that would serve as the preliminary orders for the patient, without even contacting the supervising physician.

If you are forced to deal with similar issues, discuss them with hospital or organizational administrators; they have patient care ramifications and may also cause accuracy or efficiency issues. If you are successful in being heard, you'll get some satisfaction from the experience. I was able to modify and improve some of the protocols we used at one hospital system. It created a real sense of empowerment and was a very fulfilling experience, while also enhancing patient care.

Another example of a physician regaining autonomy involves a physician I know who stopped accepting the insurance of one carrier that caused significant problems with pre-authorizations, denial of services, and paperwork. Where you have an option, remove unnecessary obstacles and make your day easier. This can reduce job stress and make your working environment more pleasant.

ACKNOWLEDGMENT AND ACCEPTANCE

On the other side of the spectrum, physicians will have to acknowledge and accept that some issues cannot be changed. Dr. Don Jacobson, a psychiatrist with experience in physician burnout, states one of the main ways physicians can begin their path to recovery from burnout is to acknowledge some things are outside of their control, particularly if they work in a hospital system.

As we mentioned in an earlier chapter, the difference between an idealistic medical student's preconceived notion of what medical practice should be, and what it actually is, can be irreconcilable. Some things are simply beyond a physician's control. EMR systems are a critical example of this. You can learn to maximize your use of these systems, or you can waste time and energy complaining about them. Accepting the things you can't change is a step forward, as much as deciding some problems are worth solving.

I suggest making a list of all the problems currently affecting your clinic or work area. Eliminate those problems with insurmountable barriers. Determine which problems **you can actually do something about** and make a concerted effort to change by formulating a plan with your coworkers and subordinates. Define and monitor tractable metrics to measure your progress.

As an example, I worked with my team to streamline tracking and reporting patient lab results. Originally, I personally reviewed thousands of labs for all of my patients. We decided my staff would do a preliminary review, and flag any with significant abnormalities for my attention. This saved me many hours. Similarly, my staff screened the large volume of postal mail, which was mostly junk mail, and gave me only the pertinent mail I needed to see.

The same approach may work to address patient emails, allowing you to spend time only on those your staff has identified as needing your expertise.

CHAPTER 26

CREATE A POSITIVE ENVIRONMENT

In my clinic, we began working toward a supportive, friendly, flexible working environment. We communicated well and I strove to recognize and acknowledge any successes and progress made by my staff. I also provided the opportunity for growth and development for those working under me, and I always provided them with open honest feedback. We soon became a clinic where others wanted to work. Some of the best nurses in the hospital eventually came to work in my clinic. In addition to making my job more pleasant, my patients and my staff significantly benefitted in the process.

CHAPTER 27

RESOLVE WORKPLACE CONFLICTS

In my marriage, my wife and I have a rule that we never go to bed angry with each other. I think a similar rule should apply to interactions with other physicians and workplace administrators—don't leave for the day without resolving issues that have flared up.

If another physician does something inappropriate, address the issue at an acceptable time in a calm, nonjudgmental fashion. Before discussing the matter with the other party, try to analyze the problem from their vantage point. When the discussion occurs, focus on areas of potential mutual agreement and thank them for listening, no matter the outcome. I employed this technique when advising a hospitalist physician recently. He told me he felt "dumped on" by other services and was asked to absorb mind-numbing paperwork and unpleasant tasks on their behalf. He subsequently communicated his feelings and received what he felt to be sincere apologies, and more importantly, a change in behavior from the other physicians he spoke with.

INAPPROPRIATE REFERRALS

Physicians are occasionally asked to see patients for consultation outside the physician's area of expertise. This expends significant staff resources, and is a waste of the patient's time and money. As a rheumatologist, pain management patients were sometimes referred to me. Pain management issues can be extremely challenging, and I have no training in that area.

After I determined the patient did not have an underlying rheumatologic condition, I referred them back to the physician who had originally referred them to me. I communicated in a pleasant but forthright way that the patient's pain management issue would be better served by a pain management consultant. The hospital system I worked in eventually partnered proactively with me to underscore to referring physicians that I was not a pain management consultant, and we eliminated the majority of these consultations.

The same rule applies for procedures. If a patient needs a procedure that falls outside a physician's comfort zone, he or she should refer them to interventional radiology, an academic institution, or the appropriate specialist with the experience to perform the procedure. For example, I occasionally had patients referred to me specifically for procedures such as muscle biopsies, which fell outside the scope of my training. I referred them to the appropriate specialist and informed the referring physician that I did not perform this type of procedure.

If you are significantly outside your comfort zone performing a certain procedure, you should not do it. Communicate to the referring clinicians that you are uncomfortable seeing referrals for that type of procedure.

CHAPTER 27

In summary, you should communicate grievances early and not let them fester. You should do so in a professional manner. Clearly articulating to your colleagues the consults you want to see and procedures you want to perform allows you to practice the type of medicine that is ideal for you.

In my case, I want to manage autoimmune disease, rheumatoid arthritis, osteoarthritis and osteoporosis, and did not want to manage chronic pain. By clearly articulating these goals with other providers, I was able to set up this type of practice.

ADMINISTRATIVE ISSUES

Physicians also can and should clearly articulate problems with hospital administrators. Unfortunately, we may view hospital administrators as purveyors of needless bureaucracy that restrict our ability to treat our patients. It's important to remember you both have the same goals, and remember healthcare executives are overseeing sometimes limited resources. At times I would scapegoat the administration of my system, and stereotype them as paper pushers with little practical utility. This type of pejorative thinking was not accurate, nor in my best long-term interest.

In the grand scheme of things it may be inevitable for a "Hatfields versus McCoys" mentality to develop in modern medicine, as the administrators oversee a finite amount of funds while patient needs and potential expenditures are almost limitless. Once I recognized this fact, it changed my interactions with administrators.

In my interactions with administrators, in contrast to some of my colleagues, I tried to communicate in a way that would resolve rather than inflame conflict. I do not approach administrators as adversaries, but rather as collaborative partners. If possible, I try to prepare an economic rational and a spreadsheet explaining my thought process to administrators. I approach them in a friendly, courteous, and non-threatening way.

CHAPTER 28

START BURNOUT PREVENTION IN MEDICAL SCHOOLS

In the process of learning to care for others, medical students commonly neglect their own wellbeing. During medical school, every trainee experiences physical deprivation, such as skipping meals and working while ill or sleep-deprived. A study at the Mayo Clinic demonstrated that although medical students enter their training with similar mental health to peers from college, as they progress through medical education, they show higher levels of mental distress and depression. The same study also showed 11% of medical students experienced symptoms of suicidal ideation and up to 50% had symptoms of depression. And more troubling, the students who were the most depressed were frequently the least likely to reach out for help.[30]

Dr. Pamela Wible relates the jaw-dropping experience of a colleague's introduction to clinical medicine. As a first year medical student, this physician remembers how her anatomy instructor made a caustic remark about a student who had attempted suicide by slashing his wrists. The instructor proceeded to demonstrate how to do it properly, if that was ever their intent. More on this topic can be found at http://www.idealmedicalcare.org/.

Physicians first learn in medical school that their mental health is not a paramount concern. In fact, medical students learn to compartmentalize mental health issues and keep them out of view. This is where the culture of medicine must change. Mental health issues should be regarded in the same light as treating high cholesterol or thyroid disease. Medical schools need to more proactively identify students in need and provide them with the necessary resources.

During the third year of medical school students are exposed to their first hands-on clinical experience. They often work with exasperated residents who are extremely sleep deprived and fatigued. It is at this juncture that a foxhole mentality can take hold. Residents can depersonalize and mock patients and display a lack of empathy. Patients become labels. They are no longer people but the "drug addict," "the alcoholic," "the loser."

I witnessed such behavior as a medical student and even remember one resident describing the patients we followed as "our enemies." One time, as a medical student when we were waiting in the ER for an ambulance to arrive with a possible admission to the cardiology service, my resident whispered softly to me, "God I hope they just code and die in the ambulance so we don't have to admit somebody else." Watching your mentors demean patients was obviously terribly discouraging, but it was easy to empathize with the residents who were tired and overworked. Some of the burned out mindset of exhausted residents seeped in to my view of patients as if by osmosis. Eventually, I was making caustic jokes and imitating patients in the break room along with my superiors.

Medical school is also a time where trainees are inevitably exposed to a truly hostile work place. While I had great experiences, like my pediatric and psychiatry rotations, I also was exposed to intimidating, unfriendly physicians in other rotations that threw instruments and swore at me. My experience was not remotely unique. During my time in medical school, these difficult physicians were tolerated because of their proficiency as doctors, despite the fact that they behaved reprehensibly toward staff, medical students, and sometimes even patients.

These types of abusive experiences can be quite traumatic when intelligent, compassionate people in their twenties work in an environment supervised by cynical and sometimes outright hostile older physicians. It creates severe distress, and students may question the path they have chosen in life. No wonder studies are demonstrating declining empathy and increased skepticism and burnout amongst medical students. One long-term aspirational goal we have at Heal Thyself MD is to let medical students know they are not alone in those feelings, and give them the tools and resources to carry on in their studies.

FINANCIAL EDUCATION

Medical schools can significantly help their students by providing financial guidance. Many students graduate from school with overwhelming debt. Some even feel compelled to go into high paying subspecialties because of it.

Medical schools should include elective options where students can learn how to set financial goals for future income, loan payback, and retirement savings. For example, many students and young clinicians don't know if they should start saving in a retirement plan before paying off their medical school debt. If students understand their personal financial situation and how to plan for the future, they can avoid making deleterious career decisions caused by debt anxiety.

CHAPTER 29

TAKE A LOOK AT MEDICAL RESIDENCY

Medical Residency is an extraordinarily intense experience. According to an article in the Archives of General Psychiatry, 4% of trainees begin their intern year with symptoms of major depression. By the end of their intern year, a staggering 25% of trainees report symptoms consistent with this condition.[31] The question that arose in my mind after reviewing these results was if 25% of interns are experiencing symptoms by the end of their first year, what is that number by the end of their third year?

Residency at times can be completely overwhelming. At one of the training programs I attended, we experienced the tragic suicide of a trainee.

Multiple studies have demonstrated a high rate of burnout in medical residents. The number of residents experiencing symptoms was frequently higher than 50%. Higher debt level has been associated with higher levels of burnout.

Studies show—and it has become universally acknowledged in the medical community—that higher rates of medical error occur among burned out residents compared to their peers, just as we have seen in physicians. Looking at it from another angle, after a medical error occurs, depression and burnout rates go up in residents. Medical error and burnout become a chicken versus the egg scenario. Which occurs first: the burnout or the error, since they both feed into each other?

With the advent of new working regulations and hour requirements, the number of consecutive hours a resident can work is limited. Residents are also guaranteed free time away from the hospital. These are positive steps—and some studies have suggested these measures have resulted in some improvement in residents' quality of life, and potentially reduced burnout. However, just like balancing a teeter totter, the reduction in resident work hours has been passed along to attending physicians, who have absorbed the additional work load. This may contribute to burnout on their side of the equation.

The most significant intervention that needs to occur in medical schools is removal of the cultural emphasis on self-sacrifice and stigmatization of mental health issues. Residents, worried that they may be perceived as weak or even worse, the unpardonable sin of requiring someone to cover their shifts if they need help, are frequently unwilling to engage in self-care behavior. They never dare ask for time off and can isolate themselves.

Isolation and burnout tend to feed into each other in a negative self-sustaining loop. Isolated residents can have the false impression that their colleagues are not experiencing the same emotions and self-doubt.

Tragically, a burned out resident in one of my training programs came to be known as "007"; like James Bond, he was licensed to kill. This resident took incomplete histories, performed shoddy, cursory exams, and after one patient died due to an error he made, he finally admitted to major problems with burnout.

The single most important message I want to deliver is this: a resident who is in trouble should not be afraid or embarrassed to admit it. Junior interns may benefit from a mentorship program with more senior residents. Support groups overseen by an outside professional could also be very helpful. Sabbatical days or meetings where interns and residents are allotted designated time off to talk about issues of physician wellness can communicate more open acceptance of the challenging work environment.

Mandating educational programs about issues like financial debt, burnout, and principles of self-care can more adequately prepare new physicians. Added flexibility for residents needing time off is pivotal to creating a more nurturing environment. Finally, emphasizing the importance of family and work-life balance by holding events for families away from the hospital will reinforce the principle that residents must have a life outside of medicine to avoid burnout.

Stanford University is a good example of a residency proactively addressing the issue of physician wellness. Counseling and mentoring are offered and residents have access to a twenty-four hour hotline for mental health consultation. Additionally, a residency peer support program has been established where the house staff can discuss bad patient outcomes.[32]

Over the next ten to fifteen years, our goal at Heal Thyself MD is to change the culture of medicine. Sadly, some potentially deleterious traits such as extreme compulsiveness and self-denial can be rewarded and result in enhanced professional success during training. These traits are not sustainable over the course of a thirty to forty year career. Our mission is to destigmatize mental health issues in physicians, and humanize our training programs at both the medical school and residency training level.

One physician recently suggested the grueling trial of residency sets a bar of low expectations for physician self-care that can be subconsciously carried into professional life—and exploited by hospital systems that do not emphasize physician wellness.

This physician worked in a fairly toxic work place and he told me, "The only reason a place like this coal mine can survive is because of residency. Think about it. Residency is like the minor leagues of pro baseball. We are exploited and denied basic human needs like sleep for three or four years. The organization I work for realizes this and they just load it on now. They figure they can pile on more stress, more requirements, more paperwork, and more burdens. After all, I made it through medical residency." At Heal Thyself MD, we are working diligently so this statement will no longer be true at either end.

CHAPTER 30

BREAK THROUGH ORGANIZATIONAL BARRIERS

Einstein: "You cannot solve a problem with the same thinking that created it."

Most treatments, interventions, and impetus for change in physician burnout management have occurred at the individual physician level. As physician practices move toward consolidation with hospital organizations, monitoring physician satisfaction and proactively addressing burnout is imperative. Successful management of the problem will enable improved patient outcomes, patient satisfaction, cost containment, and the long term success of these organizations.

ATTITUDE ADJUSTMENT ON BOTH SIDES

In our current healthcare environment, an almost built-in animosity exits between physicians and healthcare administrators. Physicians want to perform their job in a stress-free environment without significant interference or onerous regulation. Speaking from a doctor's standpoint, physicians sometimes stereotype hospital administrators as over-compensated

MBAs with no clinical knowledge who are imposing excessive bureaucracy on physicians. This kneejerk response is wrong—and ignores the considerable skills many administrators possess and the fact that they are stuck with the onerous task of implementing complex new regulations with limited resources.

As physicians, we want to be left alone to provide good care to our patients. Our anger is commonly, and sometimes unjustifiably, pointed in the direction of the closest identifiable manager, as opposed to an anonymous insurance industry, a government regulator, or a distant politician formulating deleterious health care policy. We sometimes want to "kill the messenger." We need to accept administrators as partners and approach interactions with an open mind.

However, I have seen true institutional negligence and blatant disregard for the wellbeing of the physicians who work there. A physician recently told me, "My whole life has become my job and the system I work at wants it that way."

Hopefully, by openly acknowledging the potential for adversarial interactions between physicians and hospital administrators, both sides can come together. Rather than looking at each other with suspicion, we can transform this relationship from a close-minded feud into a partnership, and work together collaboratively for the benefit of all. This will require time, effort, and commitment from both groups.

INSTITUTIONAL BARRIERS TO TREATMENT

One of the more significant institutional barriers to treatment is a lack of awareness of the problem of physician burnout. Other organizations may recognize the problem, but choose to ignore it. One recent survey of stressed physicians showed only 17% of their organizations had attempted to address the issue of physician burnout.[33] Large bureaucratic institutions by their very design can create a barrier to effective treatment. When the problem is recognized, it can be difficult to determine who is in charge of dealing with it.

Some institutions, in my experience, professed to take the problem seriously, but when I asked to speak with the designated point person, I heard only the sound of chirping crickets. In large organizations with responsibilities spread over hundreds or even thousands of people, unless someone is designated responsible or the "owner" for an issue, it stays unresolved. People will pass it around like a hot potato.

The initial concern that addressing it will negatively impact a company's bottom line, as an up-front expenditure or de-creased productivity (e.g., if a physician reduces patient volume or takes time off for recovery), is also a barrier. However, given the significantly decreased productivity, increased medical errors, higher malpractice rates, lower patient satisfaction scores, and increased physician turnover caused by physician burnout, hospital organizations ignore this problem at their own financial peril. And, once they understand the problem's scope, they'll realize the issue already has negatively impacted the bottom line.

NEW PARADIGM

On a broad national level, the current institutional approach to physician burnout is not working. Before we highlight some of the positive things we believe can be done, and the positive initiatives implemented by some organizations, we must acknowledge that a conceptual change and paradigm shift in the management of physician burnout is needed at the hospital system level.

Currently, the management of physician burnout at an institutional level is akin to the navigational and philosophical paradigm in place when the world was believed to be flat. At Heal Thyself MD, we aim to replace the ignorance, inertia, and fear of change at the organizational level with the discovery of a new prototype for the treatment of physician burnout. We are engaging with practical and empathic systems to show institutions a new model, similar to the paradigm shift that occurred when people recognized the world was in fact round. We expect this evolving, iterative process to unfold over the next decade.

Organizations that commit to prescriptive change will benefit both from an economic and a moral standpoint. For example, it has been estimated it will cost an organization $250,000 to replace a fulltime physician who leaves his practice.[34] This is a great chance for an organization to "do well by doing good." A physician recently underscored this sentiment when he told me, "I am a better, more productive doctor when I feel supported by the organization where I work."

ACKNOWLEDGMENT OF THE PROBLEM

The first step in addressing the issue of physician burnout at an institutional is to acknowledge the problem exists—just as it is for individuals. I have heard administrators express concern that acknowledging the problem of physician burnout will encourage accusations that the institution caused, or at least contributed to, the problem. After speaking with a multitude of physicians about this concern, I have found their reaction to be the polar opposite. Physicians are extraordinarily grateful and feel valued when the institution acknowledges the issue.

An acknowledgement reinforces a value alignment between the physician and the institution, creating common ground. Additionally, it clearly communicates to physicians that burnout is everyone's problem and not an individual failing.

During the acknowledgement stage, the organization should state multiple times and in different ways that they not only recognize the prevalence and seriousness of the problem, but also want to work with physicians to mitigate it. To be successful in managing burnout, hospital organizations must encourage physicians to seek support and characterize that as a healthy step.

CHAPTER 31

MAP THE ORGANIZATIONAL ANTI-BURNOUT PROGRAM

Once an organization acknowledges the problem, they can start addressing it by defining areas of improvement.

An organization must prioritize the wellness of its physicians and staff as much as it does patient satisfaction. The benefits may reach far beyond the initial goal. Remember Dr. Don Jacobson's words; "Happy doctors make for happy patients and vice versa."

MAKE BURNOUT REDUCTION AN ORGANIZATIONAL MISSION

Incorporate burnout reduction and prevention into companywide goals. Physician—as well as other staff—wellbeing improvement should be included in the organizational mission statement. Top level administrators should focus on the importance of physician burnout and communicate their commitment to address it.

DESIGNATE RESPONSIBILITY AND DISCUSS RESOURCES

Organizations should demonstrate their commitment to addressing burnout by designating a leader who will be *in charge* of the burnout management program. This "burnout administrator" should communicate the organization's intentions to physicians, even before specific plans are developed. This gives physicians an opportunity to make suggestions in the planning stage, and that will further enhance the positive impact of the acknowledgement. The organization should set up meetings at three- or six-month intervals for follow up discussion with quantifiable metrics for evaluating the implemented strategies.

SURVEYS

Many healthcare organizations have prioritized measuring patient satisfaction with surveys. A similar priority should be made to gauge satisfaction among its physicians.

Regularly scheduled anonymous surveys can be valuable tools in assessing physician burnout and quality of life issues. Surveys provide important data and can serve as a measurement tool for changes implemented.

Surveys should touch on both positive aspects an organization is getting "right" and areas needing improvement. By highlighting only positive results, problem areas can be obscured. Physician morale has been positively impacted at institutions that honestly and forthrightly address areas where improvement is needed.

If an organization wants to further boost morale and foster an aura of caring about its physicians, it should conduct a survey of physicians' spouses. Sometimes more information about physicians' work environment and work-life balance can be elicited from spouses of physicians than from the physicians themselves.

CHAPTER 31

Once the survey results are reviewed, prioritize where to begin changes, based on the biggest potential impact on physician quality of life measures.

When a change initiative is based on survey results, make sure physicians are involved in the deliberations and decision process. It may be easiest to start with one or two major change initiatives. Set up tangible benchmarks to measure progress and report results in a transparent fashion. The goal should be to exceed expectations and create a program with sufficient impact to change the institutional culture.

ONBOARDING WITH COUNSELOR

Another recent strategy implemented by some systems is "onboarding" with a counselor. Onboarding is a process designed to introduce new hires to the organization's culture before they start working there. It's usually part of orientation, and some forward-thinking organizations are introducing physicians to the dedicated burnout expert they retain during the onboarding process.[35] By communicating upfront that the organization recognizes burnout is a serious problem, they can immediately create a caring atmosphere. Physicians will feel more comfortable requesting counseling and will know exactly where to go, should they experience symptoms.

ADMINISTRATIVE SUPPORT

A healthcare system can support its physicians in many ways. Hiring medical scribes to assist with EMR documentation tasks can positively impact both patient and physician satisfaction. One of the systems I worked at created a special paperwork division that filled out many of the forms, such as insurance prior authorizations or long disability evaluations, which can bog a physician down and take time away from patient care.

ADDITIONAL ANCILLARY STAFF

When a physician asks for additional staff help, it's usually a sign his clinic is becoming very busy. Even if a hospital administrator must deny the request due to limited resources, listening to the physician and understanding the circumstances makes a tremendous difference. If the administrator can compromise and get the physician part-time help, or a medical assistant instead of a nurse, the physician will appreciate that the administrator is making an effort.

Organizations can also assist when difficulty arises with a staff member. For example, at one large healthcare organization, several employees in our clinic demonstrated problem behavior. One such employee likely was an alcoholic who was plagued by frequent absenteeism and poor quality work. When I tried to address the issue with him directly, he was nonresponsive. I then asked the organization to intervene.

The nurse was mandated to participate in a recovery program and underwent periodic binding evaluations thereafter. This nurse demonstrated a significant improvement in his behavior and professionalism as a result of the organization's intervention.

BURNOUT SPECIALIST

Some facilities have employee assistance programs with a designated counselor who works with staff on issues of substance abuse. Burnout issues should be handled similarly. Large hospital systems should train and designate a burnout specialist.

For example, Florida Hospital System designated Dr. Herdley Paolini to manage the problem of physician burnout. Dr. Paolini started a program called Physician Support Services.

I recently spoke with Dr. Paolini to get her perspective on how this program worked. To familiarize herself with the problem of physician burnout, Dr. Paolini completely immersed herself in the lives of the physicians who worked at her institution. She followed physicians in their offices and observed them in the operating room. She was there late at night when they were called for emergencies. She came to a unique understanding of what life was like for physicians and gained a first-hand perspective on burnout. The physicians who came to see Dr. Paolini benefitted from her knowledge. Subsequently, she has become a nationally recognized figure in the field of burnout management.

Physician Support Services now has a full time staff and provides physician counseling, seminars, retreats, and family counseling. Approximately 600 physicians have utilized Physician Support Services for counseling assistance, resulting in over 10,000 visits during the past decade.[36] The program has had a dramatic impact on physicians, their families, their patients, and by extension, the staff who work alongside them.

BRING IN AN EXPERT

Another avenue for healthcare systems to address the problem of burnout is to bring in experts. Some systems are using third party consultants to review their working environment and make prescriptive recommendations for workplace improvement.

CHAPTER 32

LOOK AT THE INSTITUTIONAL DAILY JOB

WORKPLACE FACILITIES

Creating convenient and considerate workplace facilities and services signals an organization's commitment to its physicians in a compelling way. Onsite exercise rooms and daycare are paramount for physician wellness. Dedicated physician lunchrooms and parking lots are additional benefits.

More important than the lunchroom and the quality of the food it serves, is having a CEO who ensures the physicians working for him or her spend an hour away from their clinical responsibilities for lunch every day. Also, a good CEO and upper level managers should have a visible presence. They should be directly observing what goes on in clinics and the ER.

COMMUNICATION

A CEO at one hospital I worked at made a point of setting up monthly lunches with physicians, where they could voice concerns or suggestions directly to him. Even when he couldn't make some of the changes recommended, physicians felt their grievances had truly been heard and acknowledged. He also made a point of getting to know the physicians who worked for him on a personal level, which improved physician morale. Additionally, every year this CEO stopped by my clinic on my birthday to give me a card, as he did for most physicians in the system. This was a small but tangible gesture which the physicians appreciated. This system also had an anonymous suggestion box for physicians' recommendations. Several major change initiatives resulted from this setup. Physicians felt listened to and appreciated at this organization.

Successful systems also do everything in their power to facilitate communication between physicians and administrators. When such systems implement a major change initiative, physicians are included in the decision-making process so their voices can be heard. This also enhances physician "buy-in" to the implemented changes.

Additionally, successful systems have established protocols for a mediation procedure to address conflicts between a physician and his administrative supervisor. I have participated in such procedures and when done well, a potentially toxic situation can be resolved in a healthy and positive fashion. It can be amazingly easy to accomplish with skilled mediators, through supervised direct and honest communication between the physician and administrator. Good communication starts with the ability to listen and reflect the feelings of the other party involved in the equation.

Some physicians have told me administrative leaders with frontline clinical experience, such as physicians or nurses, enhance the rapport with practicing physicians. Also, physicians show enhanced satisfaction and morale when the administration employs a fair approach to change initiatives, and allows physicians to maintain as much autonomy as possible.

FAMILY INVOLVEMENT

To engage physicians, organizations must demonstrate commitment to a physician's highest priority: his family. An organization should plan family-oriented, kid-friendly events. Additionally, a physician's spouse should have access to the organization's burnout mental health specialist, to discuss issues related to their spouse and impact on the family.

PHYSICIAN WELLNESS COMMITTEE AND RETREATS

Hospital systems can show respect by providing robust fiscal support for their physician wellness committees. Additionally, some systems provide physician retreats, which can be an excellent way for physicians to recharge, and connect with colleagues outside of the office. Some systems even provide accommodations and activities for the physicians' spouses and children.

PRODUCTIVITY

Productivity is perhaps the largest potential source of conflict and value misalignment between physicians and hospital systems. Instead of compensating physicians for quality of care, many of our current healthcare system pay for quantity of tests and procedures performed, and number of patients seen. Increasing patient volume can drastically decrease quality of care.

For example, I recently spoke with a family physician who saw seventeen patients in his morning clinic. This translates to a patient every ten minutes. Given the complexity of disease and number of problems some of his patients had, it was virtually impossible for him to do a thorough, competent job.

Multiple studies, including a recent one by the RAND Corporation[37], have demonstrated that one source of frustration among physicians occurs when they don't have the time to provide appropriate, quality care for their patients is one major source of burnout.

Some hospital systems still push their physicians with productivity goals. This leaves physicians feeling they are widget makers, compensated on how many patients they can "churn and burn" in an hour. However, some systems do recognize the importance of value-based, quality care. Financial incentives such as bundling of services can enhance this shift toward quality rather than quantity of care.

ABOVE ALL, DEVELOP MUTUAL RESPECT

Several initiatives have demonstrated success in promoting physician wellbeing. An organization can show respect for its physicians by making an effort not to schedule meetings that interfere with family time at nights or on the weekends. Some organizations provide their physicians the opportunity for sabbaticals. Also, organizations that reward physicians for contributions to organizational success tend to do well.

For example, at one workplace, I received a signed thank you note from the CEO of the hospital every time I received a patient compliment. This small acknowledgment boosted my morale and made me feel appreciated. Many organizations give feedback only when negative issues arise; it can be refreshing when they emphasize positive feedback. Additional gestures like "Doctor's Day" cards and thank you notes are small gestures of gratitude and appreciation an administration can show toward its physicians.

The leaders at institutions with low burnout rates model balance and emphasize the importance of work-life equilibrium. These institutions also foster an environment of honest communication with regular opportunity for feedback. Such institutions focus on creating an environment of "health" for employees as well as for their patients.

I recently worked with a hospital system that set up a physician's forum, where they can come together in support groups to talk about burnout in a supportive, non-stigmatized environment. During these meetings, physicians can also learn about what their peers' "exhausters" are, as well as about developing strategies for resilience. A physician at one of these gatherings told me, "I am truly impressed the organization is doing something about burnout. This will make it easier to come to work tomorrow morning."

CHAPTER 33

DEFINE NEW PRACTICE MODELS

Some physicians have chosen to adopt new and novel practice models and have experienced recovery from burnout and a renewed joy in the practice of medicine. In 2005, Pam Wible opened an "ideal practice" after conducting several town hall meetings in her local community of Eugene, Oregon. Dr. Wible had become burned out in her previous practice as an employed physician. After she elicited advice on what the patients in her community really wanted from their physician, and she analyzed her own needs as a clinician, she opened the first "ideal" clinic in the country.

Dr. Wible's model has subsequently been adopted around the country. Dr. Wible exemplifies a burned out physician who reclaimed her life and is now much happier both as a person and as a clinician. Dr. Wible describes her situation in her characteristically droll way: "I went from suicidal to successfully self-employed in six weeks." She invites other physicians to use her clinic as a model and in the process, "heal your patients and yourself." Learn more at http://www.idealmedicalcare.org/.

Some physicians have opened "concierge" practices. Concierge medicine is a practice model in which patients pay an annual retainer to their physician, who will provide a more enhanced level of care. This model can also be referred to as "direct primary care" when it involves a family practice or internal medicine physician. On the physician side, it eliminates the hassles of dealing with insurance carriers and allows physicians to concentrate primarily on the practice of medicine. On the patient side, it allows for greater access, unlimited in some cases, to their doctor either in person, by phone or by email.

Although every American is required to carry insurance under the Affordable Care Act, the direct primary care model enables people to save money. They can purchase less expensive health insurance policies that cover only major issues, such as hospitalizations or surgeries.

A good friend of mine opened a clinic similar to a concierge practice and he has never been happier. He tells me he really enjoys his work compared to his prior experience. He has much greater control in his career than he ever thought possible. He told me, "I am happier. My patients love me and I like being a doctor again."

I found another group of physicians who are very happy in a surprising location: the Veterans Administration (VA). A recent survey by the RAND Corporation found that physicians who provide high quality care are more satisfied professionally.[38] Many physicians at the VA feel they are able to provide higher quality care with fewer obstacles and hassles, such as significant concerns about medical liability, which their peers in the private sector face. The VA also has had an EMR system in place for many years that is judged to be very successful and relatively easy to navigate. When I was at the Albuquerque VA over twelve years ago, I found the EMR system to be wonderful, and probably the best I have ever worked with to date.

Lower staff turnover at the VA compared to the private sector is another advantage. The fact that the doctors are happier is reflected in higher patient satisfaction scores at the VA compared to the private sector. Doctors at the VA work predictable schedules and are not forced to contend with billing headaches and much of the paperwork that can make private practice so unappealing.[39] Plus, having had the privilege of practicing at a VA hospital, I cannot think of a more thankful, generous patient population than our military veterans.

These are just some of the ways physicians have moved away from a traditional employment model and creatively taken charge of their own careers. Although this may not be for everyone, some of the ideas coming out of this movement could be incorporated into more traditional models.

CHAPTER 34

GET SUPPORT FROM FAMILY AND FRIENDS

I think one of the best predictors of a physician's ability to make it through burnout is their willingness to reach out for help. Physicians who isolate themselves can end up in a downward spiral of worsening burnout.

During the recognition and acknowledgment phases of burnout, family and friends can honestly assert and observe what you may have chosen to hide or ignore. They bear first-hand witness to the decreasing energy, the waning enthusiasm, the decreased involvement in social activities, and sometimes even the increased alcohol or drug use burned out physicians may choose as a coping mechanism. They may not have all the answers, but a sympathetic ear or a reassuring hug can make all the difference when you are in crisis.

Once friends and family are aware of a physician's predicament, they can monitor for warning signs of suicide or irrational behavior, and enlist professional support. Additionally, they will be able to check in periodically with a physician who may have reached out but then choses to self-isolate thereafter.

While in recovery, the support and encouragement of family and friends can play an important part. The best thing they can offer is the ability to honestly listen. Physicians carry tremendous baggage and have bottled up some very difficult professional experiences. Simply allowing them to tell their own story, in their own way and at their own pace can prove incredibly cathartic.

Also, friends and family are able to see things from a different vantage point and may be able to offer several helpful suggestions to a physician experiencing burnout. And, they are usually willing to help out with errands and other tasks while a physician implements major life changes.

Reaching out for help and acknowledging the problem to friends and family is a courageous act for any physician to make. This initial step can be challenging and frightening. Perhaps the most important tools friends and family have are the simple acts of giving comfort and support. My family repeatedly told me, "You will get through this." They were right.

CHAPTER 35

LET YOUR CLOSEST ONE IN

Most physicians' closest relationship is with their spouse or significant other. They know what is going through a physician's mind, and experience firsthand the sadness and despair of physician burnout. In my experience, no other relationship is so pivotal in the management of physician burnout.

One husband recently told me how his wife was suffering in silence. He said, "I am so sorry for our kids. She is in such pain and they are suffering because they can see Mommy is so unhappy. She comes home from work exhausted and now has to do all of this electronic charting during her supposed time off. I am really worried about her. She cannot go on like this."

A loving, supportive spouse can be pivotal to the burnout recovery process. Often, the spouse has suffered alongside the physician for years and witnessed a change in the character of the person they married.

Sometimes the contempt a physician feels about his work situation or toward patients can spill over into his interactions with his family. My wife aptly summed it up, "It was really hard watching you live that life. It felt like something in you had died." Slowly, I had drifted out of my wife and daughter's lives as I became engulfed in burnout. Although I attended my daughter's birthday parties and dance recitals, I was not fully present. I was obsessing about a sick lupus patient or waiting for my pager to go off. Sunday nights were filled with despair, as I anticipated another work day.

For physicians who are married or involved in a relationship, they need the support of their spouse or other important person, to make major life changes and commit to burnout recovery. I have observed that physicians in dysfunctional marriages tend to suffer more in burnout, whereas those in supportive relationships do markedly better.

A spouse or life partner who is there to nurture you through both good times and bad will greatly ease a transition through this rocky period. They can also check in with you to make sure you are progressing. They are willing to accommodate major life changes—you will get complete "buy in" from them because they have been unhappy and suffering in silence themselves. Speaking from my own personal experience, my wife encouraged and supported me every step of the way and I never could have made it without her.

At Heal Thyself MD, we include assistance for the spouses and family members as part of burnout management. Many of them have suffered as well. I am honored to work alongside my wife Rachel in this enterprise. Find more information about spouse and family support at tommurphymd.com.

CHAPTER 36

GET SUPPORT FROM SPONSORS, COUNSELORS, AND COACHES

Isolation complicates burnout and contributes to worsening symptoms. When a physician is feeling maximally burned out, it is very important he or she reach out for support from family, friends, coworkers, and peers. A counselor or coach can also be immensely helpful at this time.

COMMUNITY OF SUPPORT

While in recovery from burnout, I learned that support can come from many sources. Peers, in the form of sponsors or mentors, provide valuable perspective. Psychologists, psychiatrists, and life coaches can teach skills and coping methods for working through any burnout issue.

No two physicians experiencing burnout are exactly alike. A treatment plan should be tailored to suit the needs and goals for each individual physician. I am extremely grateful to the psychologist I worked with, and realize he was instrumental in my recovery.

If a physician is suffering coexisting depression, it is imperative for him or her to seek psychiatric care. And if the physician is not depressed, they may still benefit from counseling, if they view it as a proactive step.

Psychiatrists and psychologists who are experienced in the management of burnout and job-related stress can play a pivotal role in helping a physician develop a plan for a path forward out of burnout and employ appropriate and healthy coping strategies to get there.

COACHING

I have both benefited from and worked alongside coaches who specialize in helping physicians. A life coach is NOT a psychologist or psychiatrist. A life coach offers support and encouragement while helping an individual recognize roadblocks he may not have been aware of. Frequently, life coaches have gone through transformative life changes and they can be wonderful tour guides for the rest of us when we try to implement major life change.

My coach, Dr. Lisa Chu, helped me learn so much about myself through various techniques, such as journaling. With her, I prioritized the steps I needed to move forward, built healthier relationships with both friends and family, and formulated a strategy to achieve my goals. She also helped me improve time management and significantly improve my wellbeing by boosting my confidence and self-esteem. I am very grateful for her expertise and now am working with other coaches to assist struggling physicians improve their lives.

CHAPTER 37

CONNECT WITH YOUR MIND

At my most cynical stage of burnout, I considered things like journaling and meditation to be pointless and a waste of time. I now realize ten minutes of journaling and meditation a day helped me to recover from my own burnout experience. Each of these practices can be invaluable tools.

JOURNALING: WHAT SHOULD I WRITE ABOUT?

Write about whatever feels "right." You're not going to publish your journal, and you don't need an outline. Don't worry about spelling or grammar. The main thing is to commit to journaling for ten minutes every day when it's convenient for you, maybe shortly before bed or right after dinner.

In my case, I wrote about painful medical experiences from my career and how I reacted to them. You might write about working with a difficult patient or describing why you chose to go into medicine. You can journal about a difficult work day or a recent positive patient encounter. Journaling allows you to gain greater insight about yourself and your career. It can reveal anxieties, repressed thoughts and fears, as well as previously forgotten joys. When you are writing, you are in a place where you can decompress and unwind.

Working with a mentor can potentially enhance the experience of journaling. In my case, I shared what I wrote with my life coach, Dr. Lisa Chu, and she gave me invaluable insight from an outsider's point of view. Working with Lisa allowed me to acknowledge feelings of loss, grief, and guilt about patient care issues, some of which I had carried for over ten years. Some physicians may want to share what they have written with friends or family members, and others may prefer to keep their writing private and not to share it with anyone. It is really up to you.

Journaling allowed me to clarify my thoughts when I was angry or disappointed, and it also helped me to determine whether I was working towards my personal and professional goals. It allowed me to begin to process my disenchantment with medicine and my emerging burnout more clearly. When I wrote about my feelings I realized I could not, nor should I, just "suck it up" and continue working in a miserable environment. I suspect many physicians will feel the same way.

When you write about a problem, you are recording it on paper and are therefore better able to formulate plans to solve the problem, rather than simply holding on to it in a mental storage space. In the process of journaling, a person can gain insights about themselves that they would have otherwise missed. Finally, journaling allows a person the opportunity to learn from their mistakes and to track their progress.

MINDFULNESS

Mindfulness is the practice of being purposefully and non-judgmentally present in the moment. Studies have demonstrated that mindfulness can have an impact on physician burnout. And, you can use it to improve your patient interactions.

It is extraordinarily difficult in our era of attention deficit disorder medicine with its myriad distractions of pagers going off, blinking clinical alerts about abnormal lab values on a patient's EMR, and the nurse who interrupts a visit to say another doctor is on the phone who needs to speak with you right away, to simply be present in the moment with our patients.

When you are able to truly focus your attention and energy on the patient, you are practicing medicine in a meaningful way. When your mind is elsewhere, your patient can sense this and the care you deliver may not be as effective. It is extraordinarily difficult to be mindful in any situation, let alone a busy clinical medical practice.

When you are in maximum burnout, you cannot focus on the task at hand, much less process powerful, meaningful experiences such as the death of a patient or receiving a thank-you card from a patient for an office visit. Your mind is elsewhere, and patient encounters become depersonalized chores.

Outside of medicine, mindfulness has been widely recognized as a healthy way to alleviate stress and promote wellbeing. It brings attention to a selected object of focus, such as your breathing.

I tried to employ the same practice in being mindful that I brought to a task such as comforting my daughter and putting a band aid on her when she cut herself. I simply concentrated on the task at hand to the exclusion of all other things in the world. For this time, I did not worry about what my 401K was doing or what was going on in the Middle East. I simply devoted all my resources and concentration to the task at hand.

MEDITATION

Meditation is a practice which allows you to restore yourself and experience an inner peace. All of the struggles, stress, and anxiety from the day can be wiped away. It is possible to meditate anywhere, whether out on a walk in nature, or in the office with your door closed for ten minutes during your lunch hour.

Meditation enhances your emotional wellbeing. Innumerable studies have shown the beneficial impact this practice can play in psychological and physical health. In my life, meditation has been a great way to clear my mind of clutter and anxiety. The burnout experience is largely about our "fight or flight" physiologic response to stress. Mediation is a wonderful way to mitigate the deleterious impact this response has on both our body and mind.

CHAPTER 38

REDUCE STRESS BY DOING WHAT YOU LOVE

Physicians need to do things to reenergize and recharge. I think of restorative activities such as exercise, yoga, and reading (or whatever you like to do for relaxation) as imperative to a physician's health. Engaging in enjoyable activities should be part of every physician's personal burnout prevention plan.

TAKE CARE OF YOURSELF

Many physicians suffer from what I describe as the martyr syndrome. You are so busy taking care of other people that you neglect your own health. If you don't consciously choose otherwise, your life goes by at one hundred miles an hour, and you rarely take the time to recharge your own batteries. You either don't recognize (or ignore) the importance of your own energy reserves, or sometimes even feel guilty when you engage in restorative activities.

It can be easy to let these activities fall to the wayside because of your schedule. Prioritizing them has to be part of your commitment to your own wellbeing. Also, you need to go to the doctor for regularly scheduled checkups, undergo the recommended age-appropriate screening exams, and to take time off work when you are sick—just as you recommend for your patients.

Taking care of yourself is an essential part of being a good physician. It will keep you healthy and more focused when you are at work. The common refrain I always hear is: "I don't have the time." That is simply not true. **Your working environment and schedule are determined by the choices you make.**

If you continue to cram more in and say yes to every request, you won't have the time to take care of yourself—and you will assuredly burn yourself out. Now is the time to make these changes so you can spend the weekend stress-free at your daughter's dance recital, or fishing with your son, for example.

Pay attention to your body. If you aren't sleeping, your neck is always tight, or you're feeling nauseous, your body is communicating that you need a change. Make time and a commitment to do things totally unrelated to medicine. Also, allow yourself some time and space to do absolutely nothing, what I call "breathing space."

If you conceive of your career and life as a bucket full of water, there are many aspects of modern medicine that cause small holes in the bottom of this container. It is imperative that you maintain the level in your personal bucket with "bucket fillers", namely the activities you love, lest you become completely depleted.

Reclaim your life and prioritize your own health. Do what you love, whether that is fly fishing on the Boise River or a trip to Paris. Plan trips in advance and commit to them—and put them on the calendar so they become nonnegotiable. Sit down at the start of the year, make plans, and get your tickets several months ahead of time. Decide when and where you and your family **will** go on vacation this year.

Everyone will have their own way of recharging their batteries. For example, I always made time to exercise during my lunch period. I felt better, was more relaxed, and I was a better physician as a consequence. If you take care of yourself, you will be better at taking care of others.

Hopefully, this strategy along with the others we have described in this book will help you navigate through burnout—or even avoid it altogether—and discover a new, more joyful path in medicine.

Getting through burnout takes energy and commitment. But it can be done. My hope is once you've completed the journey you will rekindle that passion for medicine you once had.

Think of your career, and for that matter your life, as an hourglass. Whether you are just starting fresh out of medical school or are a year away from retirement, you can't change your past, or get back the sand that has flowed to the bottom of the glass. What you have left is the sand remaining at the top—this represents what is left of your medical career. **Your decisions and your actions** moving forward will shape how the rest of your career will unfold.

Find ways to prioritize your own wellbeing and happiness. In so doing, not only will you be a better spouse, parent, friend, or member of the community, but you can return to being the type of physician you envisioned when you were an idealistic young medical student, sitting in a lecture hall waiting for your first class to start.

EPILOGUE

Steve Jobs said, "Each morning I look in the mirror and ask myself this question: 'If today were the last day of my life, would I want to do what I am about to do today? And whenever the answer is no for too many days in a row, I know I need to change something.'"

My journey from an enthusiastic medical student to a burned out middle aged physician took nineteen years. Near the tail end of my career, I started to notice I was becoming the type of physician I never wanted to be. I was impatient and sarcastic. Occasionally, I was dismissive of my patients. I made caustic jokes about some patients in the lunchroom. I was not happy.

Patients suffer too because a disabled doctor can't deliver the type care patients deserve. Sure he can go through the motions, can prescribe the appropriate meds etc., but that's all he does. And patients intuitively sense his lack of commitment.

When a doctor is engaged, some kind of magical placebo effect occurs between the doctor and a sick patient. "Hands on" was the way the profession referred to this magic. No visit to a sick patient was complete till the physician placed his "hands on the person." The physical touch of a committed physician was thought to promote healing, to give the patient confidence in his care. Maybe this practice strikes us as a little hokey today, but the general principle still holds true.

Patients need to believe in their doctor. An empathetic touch can make all the difference and can also be the key to medical success. Danielle Ofri exemplifies this point in her book, *What Doctors Feel*, when she notes that the rate of severe diabetic complications in patients of doctors who rate high on a standard empathy scale is a remarkable 40% better than those cared for by physicians with low empathy scores. Ofri observes that this difference is comparable "to the benefits seen with the most intensive medical therapy."[40] The tragedy of burnout is that it effaces genuine empathy, spirituality and commitment. Nietze put it best: "Physician, heal thyself: then wilt thou also heal thy patient."

In my case, burnout started insidiously, like a nagging pain, and I chose to ignore it. I hope others can learn from my example. As I mentioned earlier in this book, I am a runner. Once last year, while running on a treadmill, I was really pushing myself at a fast pace and I started to notice some mild discomfort in the back of my right leg. As I kept running the twinges in my leg morphed into agonizing pain, but I pushed through and ignored what my body was trying to tell me, just as we as physicians do with burnout. We "tough it out."

What was the result with my leg? I partially tore my right hamstring and could not run normally for over three months. Don't repeat my mistake with your own burnout, waiting until it is too late to acknowledge the problem. If you feel it creeping up on you, the time for action is now. If those little twinges you feel are becoming more severe and frequent, stop at this moment and do something about it for yourself, your family and your patients before you find yourself in an emergent situation, before something irrevocable happens, before you tear your hamstring.

Making the commitment to do something about burnout can be hard. At Heal Thyself MD, I have explored the concept of learned helplessness with psychiatrist Dr. Don Jacobson, an expert in the field of burnout. Learned helplessness is a condition in which you believe a problem is permanent, that nothing can be done to solve or change it. Learned helplessness is extraordinarily common in burnout and it is a belief system that must be discarded if you hope to make progress. If you are suffering from burnout, in order to move forward and recover, you will have to change limiting beliefs that resulted in your acceptance of a clearly unhealthy job environment. Burnout does not have to be permanent. At its very essence the term burnout implies that at one point you were on fire, bursting with energy and passion for medicine. The essence of both burnout prevention and recovery is to rekindle that passion: that inner fire.

The best analogy I can think of to close this book involves a parable I recently heard about circus elephants. Grown elephants in the circus do not run away because of a small metal chain attached to one of their legs. The chain could not possibly contain these mammoth creatures. What prevents them from trying to break out of their shackle? When the elephant was a baby, a chain was affixed to its leg and connected to a peg hammered into the ground. If a baby elephant tried to break away, the chain and stake were strong enough to hold it. The baby elephant soon learned its lesson and accepted its confinement. It stopped trying to escape. The small chain and stake would never be enough to contain a full-grown animal if it tried to escape, but by the time the animal has reached adulthood, it has relinquished all hope for an escape and freedom. The adult elephant has grown to accept its fate and is fooled by the little chain around its leg. The same is true for your medical career. You can remain confined by an artificial barricade or you can experience a new found freedom. The **choice** is up to you.

ACKNOWLEDGMENTS

Great thanks go out to my mom and sister for supporting me during the process of writing this book. I thank my parents-in-law, Earl and Ros, for their kindness and untiring encouragement during this process. I reserve special thanks for my daughter Rose who served as my inspiration for writing this book. She always seems to make me laugh when I am down and she is a wonderful, beautiful gift that brightens every day.

I send great thanks to my grandfather, my father, and his brothers, Tom and David. These men form my own personal Mount Rushmore with the visages of what it means to be a doctor. Tom and David are deeply missed. I owe special thanks to their spouses, Jane and Luana, who both have a never ending spirit of generosity.

I am very grateful to Maryanna Young, Jennifer Regner, and Hannah Cross at Aloha Publishing who made this book a reality and believed in this project so strongly. Maryanna brought such passion and insight to this project and I will be forever grateful.

I send thanks to friends Jim Koslow and Elisabeth Wittman who took time out of their busy schedules to read my manuscript and help improve it.

I send thanks to Dr. Pam Wible who is working to save American medicine and who touches the lives of countless physicians each and every day. Pam, you have inspired me to rediscover that long-ago discarded medical student application essay about why I wanted to become a doctor—thank you. I also send thanks to Herdley Paolini, Kathy Gibney, and John-Henry Pfifferling, three psychologists who have saved the lives of innumerable physicians and contributed to this project. Thanks goes to Nichole Jordan from Synchronicity Counseling in Boise who also made contributions. I send thanks to Dr. Ann Cordum and Dr. Kristen Fiorentino, who showed me what it means to practice "ideal" medicine and have inspired my return to active clinical practice. I thank Dr. Cory S. Fawcett for his contributions, and Dr. Hilda Draeger and Dr. Mike Urbano for their encouragement. I send great thanks to psychiatrist and friend Dr. Don Jacobson for his support, friendship, and remarkable wisdom.

Finally, I am so grateful to my wife Rachel, who helped me get through burnout and now works alongside me at Heal Thyself MD. She truly is my inspiration and my angel. When I think of Rachel, Lou Gehrig's quote comes to mind, "I consider myself the luckiest man on the face of the earth."

ABOUT THE AUTHOR

Dr. Tom Murphy is a board certified rheumatologist who lives with his wife Rachel and their daughter Rose in Boise, Idaho. He started his medical career at Northwestern University School of Medicine in 1995. He did his internal medicine training at the University of New Mexico and his rheumatology fellowship at the University of Virginia. He has had academic experience as a mentor and teacher of residents in clinical rheumatology, and his clinical publications include the New England Journal of Medicine.

After going through his own experience with burnout, Dr. Murphy researched the topic and wrote this book to help others who may be experiencing it. He and his wife founded Heal Thyself MD in 2014 to help physicians and family members impacted by the epidemic of physician burnout. He speaks about physician burnout, works with physicians on an individual level, and consults with hospital systems to address the problem. More information about his work can be found at tommurphymd.com.

Dr. Murphy's outside interests include running, spending time with his family, American history, and sports, particularly his beloved Chicago Cubs. Ever the optimist, he is convinced that one day he and his family will watch the Cubs win the World Series.

ENDNOTES

INTRODUCTION

1. "Physician Stress and Burnout Survey." Physician Wellness Services and Cejka Search, 2011, http://www.cejkasearch.com/wp-content/uploads/physician-stress-burnout-survey.pdf.
2. Maslach, Christina, and Michael P. Leiter. *The Truth About Burnout: How Organizations Cause Personal Stress and What to Do About It* (Jossey-Bass, 2000).

CHAPTER 3

3. Maslach, C., Jackson, S., Leiter, M. *Maslach Burnout Inventory Manual, 3rd ed.* (Palo Alto, CA: Consulting Psychologists Press, 1996).

CHAPTER 4

4. Grace, Shirley. "Lifestyles: Say Goodbye to Burnout." *Physician Practice* May 1, 2001, Vol. 17 No 7.
5. Shanafelt, MD, Tait D., Sonja Boone, MD, Litjen Tan, PhD, Lotte N. Dyrbye, MD, MHPE, Wayne Sotile, PhD, Daniel Satele, BS, Colin P. West, MD, PhD, Jeff Sloan, PhD, Michael

R. Oreskovich. "Burnout and Satisfaction With Work-Life Balance Among US Physicians Relative to the General US Population." *Arch. Intern. Med.* 2012, Vol. 172 No. 18, 1377-1385.

6. "Physician Stress and Burnout Survey." Physician Wellness Services and Cejka Search, 2011, http://www.cejkasearch.com/wp-content/uploads/physician-stress-burnout-survey.pdf.

7. McMurray, MD, Julia E., Mark Linzer, MD, Thomas R. Konrad, PhD, Jeffrey Douglas, PhD, Richard Shugerman, MD, Kathleen Nelson, MD, and the SGIM Career Satisfaction Study Group. "The Work Lives of Women Physicians." *J. Gen. Intern. Med.* June 15, 2000, Vol. 15 No. 6, 372–380.

8. Houkes, Inge, Yvonne Winants, Mascha Twellaar, Petra Verdonk Houkes, et al. "Development of burnout over time and the causal order of the three dimensions of burnout among male and female GPs. A Three-Wave Panel Study." *BMC Public Health* 2011, Vol. 11, p.240. http://www.biomedcentral.com/1471-2458/11/240.

9. Dyrbye, MD, Liselotte N., Matthew R. Thomas, MD, F. Stanford Massie, MD, David V. Power, MD, Anne Eacker, MD, William Harper, MD, Steven Durning, MD, Christine Moutier, MD, Daniel W. Szydlo, BA, Paul J. Novotny, MS, Jeff A. Sloan, PhD, and Tait D. Shanafelt, MD. *"Burnout and Suicidal Ideation among U.S. Medical Students."* Ann. Intern. *Med.* 2008, Vol. 149, 334-341.

10. Survey conducted on behalf of The Physicians Foundation by Merritt Hawkins, completed September, 2012. The Physicians Foundation.

11. Survey conducted on behalf of The Physicians Foundation by Merritt Hawkins, completed September, 2012. The Physicians Foundation.

CHAPTER 5

12. Chen, MD, Pauline W. "The Widespread Problem of Doctor Burnout." *New York Times*, blog post, http://well.blogs.nytimes. com/2012/08/23/the-widespread-problem-of-doctor-burnout/)

CHAPTER 8

13. http://www.idealmedicalcare.org/.

CHAPTER 9

14. http://www.idealmedicalcare.org/blog/physician-first-do-no-harm-to-yourself/.

15. http://www.idealmedicalcare.org/blog/physician-suicide-101-secrets-lies-solutions/.

16. Andrew, Louise B., MD, JD; Chief Editor: Barry E. Brenner, MD, PhD, FACEP *Physician Suicide: Medscape,* July 17th, 2014.

CHAPTER 10

17. Jahur, Sandeep. "Why Doctors are Sick of Their Profession," *Wall Street Journal* Editorial, August 19, 2014.

18. Friedberg, Mark W. et al. "Factors Affecting Physician Professional Satisfaction and Their Implications for Patient Care, Health System, and Health Policy." 2013, RAND Corporation, http://www.rand.org/pubs/research_reports/RR439.html.

CHAPTER 11

19. A) Willcock, S. M., Daly, M. G., Tennant, C. C., Allard, B. J. "Burnout and psychiatric morbidity in new medical graduates." *Med. J. Aust.* 2004, Vol. 181, 357-360.

    B) Schattner, P. S., Davidson, N. Serry. "Doctors' health and wellbeing: taking up the challenge in Australia." *Med. J. Aust.* 2004, Vol. 181, 348-349.

CHAPTER 14

20. Grace, Shirley. "Lifestyles: Say Goodbye to Burnout." May 1, 2007, *Physician Practice*. Vol. 17 No. 7.

21. Epperly, Ted. *Fractured: America's Broken Healthcare System and What We Must do to Heal It* (New York: Sterling and Ross Publishers, 2012).

CHAPTER 15

22. Jahur, Sandeep. "Why Doctors are Sick of Their Profession," *Wall Street Journal* Editorial, August 19, 2014.

23. Friedberg, Mark W. et al. "Factors Affecting Physician Professional Satisfaction and Their Implications for Patient Care, Health System, and Health Policy." 2013, RAND Corporation, http://www.rand.org/pubs/research_reports/RR439.html.

24. Ofri, Danielle. *What Doctors Feel: How Emotions Affect the Practice of Medicine* (Beacon Press, 2013).

CHAPTER 17

25. Friedberg, Mark W. et al. "Factors Affecting Physician Professional Satisfaction and Their Implications for Patient Care, Health System, and Health Policy." 2013, RAND Corporation, http://www.rand.org/pubs/research_reports/RR439.html.

26. Survey conducted on behalf of The Physicians Foundation by Merritt Hawkins, 2008. The Physicians Foundation. Lead author of this survey and advising consultants for Merritt Hawkins & Associates were Mark Smith, President, MHA; Phillip Miller, Vice President Communications, MHA; and Kurt Mosley, Vice President Business Development, MHA. Design and layout by Steve Schaumburg, Director Marketing & Brand Strategy, MHA and Stephanie Godwin, Manager Business Development, MHA.

27. Survey conducted on behalf of The Physicians Foundation by Merritt Hawkins, completed September, 2012. The Physicians Foundation.

CHAPTER 19

28. Shanafelt, MD, Tait D., Sonja Boone, MD, Litjen Tan, PhD, Lotte N. Dyrbye, MD, MHPE, Wayne Sotile, PhD, Daniel Satele, BS, Colin P. West, MD, PhD, Jeff Sloan, PhD, Michael R. Oreskovich. "Burnout and Satisfaction With Work-Life Balance Among US Physicians Relative to the General US Population." *Arch. Intern. Med.* 2012, Vol. 172 No. 18, 1377-1385.

CHAPTER 21

29. Survey conducted on behalf of The Physicians Foundation by Merritt Hawkins, 2008. The Physicians Foundation. Lead author of this survey and advising consultants for Merritt Hawkins & Associates were Mark Smith, President, MHA; Phillip Miller, Vice President Communications, MHA; and Kurt Mosley, Vice President Business Development, MHA. Design and layout by Steve Schaumburg, Director Marketing & Brand Strategy, MHA and Stephanie Godwin, Manager Business Development, MHA.

CHAPTER 28

30. Dyrbye, MD, Liselotte N., Matthew R. Thomas, MD, F. Stanford Massie, MD, David V. Power, MD, Anne Eacker, MD, William Harper, MD, Steven Durning, MD, Christine Moutier, MD, Daniel W. Szydlo, BA, Paul J. Novotny, MS, Jeff A. Sloan, PhD, and Tait D. Shanafelt, MD. *"Burnout and Suicidal Ideation among U.S. Medical Students."* Ann. Intern. Med. 2008, Vol. 149, 334-341.

CHAPTER 29

31. Sen, Srijan, MD, PhD, Henry R. Kranzler, MD, John H. Krystal, MD, Heather Speller, MD, Grace Chan, PhD, Joel Gelernter, MD, and Constance Guille. "A Prospective Cohort Study Investigating Factors Associated With Depression During Medical Internship." *Arch. Gen. Psychiatry* 2010, Vol. 67 No. 6, 557-565.

32. Sadick, Barbara. "Physician burnout is on the rise." *Chicago Tribune*, October 14th, 2014

CHAPTER 30

33. Beaulieu-Volk, Debra. "Fierce exclusive: Physician wellness experts on combating burnout." *Fierce Practice Management*, August 21, 2012

34. Hamilton, Ted. "Physician Burnout: Health Care Systems Seek Wellness Solutions." *Publication of CHA (Catholic Health Association)* May-June 2014.

CHAPTER 31

35. Paolini, Herdley O., PhD, Burt Bertram, EdD, LMFT, LMHC, Ted Hamilton, MD, MBA. "Antidotes to Burnout: Fostering Physician Resiliency, Well-Being, and Holistic Development." *Medscape Psychiatry* April 19, 2013.

36. Hamilton, Ted. "Physician Burnout: Health Care Systems Seek Wellness Solutions." Publication of CHA (Catholic Health Association) May-June 2014.

CHAPTER 32

37. Friedberg, Mark W. et al. "Factors Affecting Physician Professional Satisfaction and Their Implications for Patient Care, Health System, and Health Policy." 2013, RAND Corporation, http://www.rand.org/pubs/research_reports/RR439.html.

CHAPTER 33

38. Friedberg, Mark W. et al. "Factors Affecting Physician Professional Satisfaction and Their Implications for Patient Care, Health System, and Health Policy." 2013, RAND Corporation, http://www.rand.org/pubs/research_reports/RR439.html.

39. Loveridge, Amy. "Professional Satisfaction for Physicians: VA Has the Factors Physicians Seek." *VA Careers* January 28th, 2014.

EPILOGUE

40. Ofri, Danielle. *What Doctors Feel: How Emotions Affect the Practice of Medicine* (Beacon Press, 2013).